E FOR ADDITIVES

THORSONS COMPLETE ADDITIVE GUIDE

E FOR ADDITIVES

THORSONS COMPLETE ADDITIVE GUIDE

Everything you should know about additives
in your food-including a comprehensive
listing of additive safe foods

Maurice Hanssen

THORSONS PUBLISHING GROUP
Wellingborough, Northamptonshire

This combined edition published 1986

ISBN 0 7225 1419 0

Printed and bound in Great Britain

Contents

This special Complete Additive Guide brings together Maurice Hanssen's No. 1 best-seller *E for Additives*, the book that started a food buying revolution, and its successful sequel *The E for Additives Supermarket Shopping Guide* making it the most comprehensive directory of food additives.

PART 1
THE E-NUMBER DECODER

Acknowledgements

This book is dedicated to those who helped make it possible:

To my Research Assistant, Jill Marsden B.Sc., whose strong will and tenacity were needed over many arduous months in our attempt to produce daylight where there was darkness.

To Elizabeth Brown and Maureen Sharp whose typing and re-typing of difficult material made my publisher's lot a happy one.

To Leslie Kenton who wrote such a thoughtful Foreword. But those who enjoy her articles in *Harpers and Queen*, and her fine books, would expect that!

About the Author

Maurice Hanssen is Chairman of the academic and parliamentary consumer group, The National Association for Health, which monitors all food and medicines legislation. He is in close contact with the development of European law relating to food, medicines and consumer affairs, and is a member of the European Food Law Association.

Foreword

This comprehensive book is one which in a sense I wish need never have been written. I would prefer to live in a world where we harvested our foods fresh from the earth, ate them immediately and never had to give a thought to food preservatives, artificial emulsifiers and stabilizers, anti-oxidants and permitted colours. Alas, we do not live in such a world. High technology food production and elaborate chains of food distribution have created a situation in which food additives are necessary. Yet for the protection of oneself and one's family it is also necessary to be well informed about these hundreds of additives in quite specific terms and highly aware of the possible implications of their inclusion in our daily diet.

I therefore welcome Maurice Hanssen's *E For Additives*. Mr Hanssen has produced a simple-to-follow yet remarkably ambitious guide which can help people make informed decisions about the foods on their supermarket shelves even before they buy them. He carefully explains both the pros and cons of food additives, clarifies the meaning of such commonly used but little understood words as 'stabilizers' and 'tenderizers', and offers a quick-to-use guide to each specific additive, its name, where it comes from, the possible adverse effects of using it and a list of typical products in which it is used. This book is a useful tool for anyone concerned about the health of himself and his family. I for one would not want to be without it.

LESLIE KENTON

Introduction

What are 'E' Numbers?

Although it is not very obvious when you go through Customs, a stated objective of the European Economic Community or Common Market is to harmonize laws.

So that foods can be moved from country to country within the Common Market, a list of additives that are generally recognized as safe has been introduced. These are the 'E' numbers. Additions are made to the list from time to time as new substances are found to be suitable for use in foods. Substances are removed from the list if they are found to present problems or if they can be replaced by a more effective substance with greater safety.

Are Additives Necessary?

Sugar and salt are perhaps the most common food additives and are very important in the preservation of foods. But excessive sugar and salt is not healthy. There is a likely relationship between too much salt and high blood pressure and between excessive sugar and dental decay as well as overweight. So their use is valuable but their consumption needs to be moderated. The same is true of most other additives — they are tested for safety — but if you read your labels carefully you can control your intake.

Quite a few of the 'E' numbers are of substances that occur in nature such as vitamin C and lecithin.

This book is to help you to decide whether the additives in your food are the sort that are essential to keep it in good condition, such as when the preservation of meat products is far more important than the risks of possibly fatal food poisoning from eating tainted meat, whether it is just to assist the manufacturing processes which produce the food, or whether it is to colour, to enhance the flavour or even to allow the manufacturer to add extra water or to hide excess fat without the awareness of the consumer.

The introduction of 'E' numbers has given us, once the code can be cracked, more detail than we have ever before been given over exactly what it is we are eating.

We have for the first time enough information appearing on labels to enable us to choose whether the additives are the sort that we are happy to use or would prefer to do without. Remember too, that although perhaps one in ten will find the yellow colour tartrazine does not suit them, nine out of ten will find that it does! Question whether the additives are just for the convenience of the manufacturer, enabling him to use lower quality raw materials or processing methods without the knowledge of the consumer, or whether they enable the food to be brought to you better tasting and in better condition than would be possible without the use of additives. The E.E.C. has been issuing Directives on additives since 1962, so learn to read the label wisely.

All foods made after 1 January 1986 will (except for flavourings) have to have the 'E' number or the actual name in the list of ingredients. Until then is a transitional period to enable manufacturers to change their packaging. The old sort of uninformative labelling with words such as 'permitted colouring' will then cease. The very word 'permitted' whilst giving a feeling of security, means very little for if the manufacturer used a colour that was *not* permitted then he would be breaking the law and, incredibly, there are no regulations covering the composition of flavours except the general requirement that a food should be safe. So there is no such thing as a permitted flavour — a serious gap in the protection of the consumer.

There would not be enough room on many products to spell out all the additives used in full without making some packs look like a food chemist's dictionary so the 'E' number idea can be very useful to the consumer especially if he or she has a sensitivity to certain additives or a desire to choose what goes into the food.

Also included in this book are numbers without the prefix 'E'. These are, at the time of writing, proposals and need not necessarily be adopted. Also some 'E' numbers are not at present permitted in Britain but are also included for the sake of completeness.

How to Use This Book

Some additives have several different uses but in general 'E' numbers follow a numerical system according to their main function. The first part of this book is laid out numerically, according to the 'E' number, so that you can quickly look up the information on the label.

Each entry lists the number, the name of the substance, its uses, any reported adverse effects, whether or not it occurs naturally and, from time to time, notes for the consumer. At the end is an alphabetical list of 'E' numbers so that any ingredient given by name instead of number can be checked out.

The labelling regulations state that ingredients, including water, must be given in descending order by weight so it is a useful indicator of the amount of the additive present to see, for example, whether it comes above or below salt.

The Ministry of Agriculture, Fisheries and Food produces a little guide to 'E' numbers which does not give any indication of what the substances are and what they do. In this book an attempt has been made to gather as much information as possible and there will inevitably be some sins of omission and indeed the E.E.C. will certainly make continual changes in their proposals. Any changes which are brought to our attention will be rectified, where appropriate, in subsequent editions. We would also be glad to know of products using additives for which we found no typical examples.

Information for the Consumer

Apart from the list of ingredients in descending order by weight and with the warning to look out for that magic ingredient water especially in products such as ham where you would not normally wish to see it, there are many safeguards for the consumer who is aware of what are the rules of the game.

Date marking is now required on most pre-packed foods (with a few exceptions, such as frozen foods, wine and vinegar) unless they have a shelf-life of at least 18 months. Even products with a very long shelf-life may be marked, but this is not mandatory. This shall be expressed as *either:*

- A best before date (day, month, year) plus storage conditions (if necessary).

Or:

- If the food has a life of between 3 months and 18 months, a best before end date (month, year).
- If the food has a 'life' of between 6 weeks and 3 months, a best before date (day, month) plus storage conditions (if necessary).
- If the food is perishable and is intended for consumption within 6 weeks of being packed, a sell by date (day, month) plus storage conditions and a storage period after purchase.

There is no reason why you should not buy overdue products, especially if they are reduced in price, because the onus is on the shopkeeper to provide goods which live up to the quality of their description, in other words they must not be bad or 'off'. With the longer time datings you are safe in buying goods that are near the end of their expiry date if the shop is clean and well maintained. However if such a product has deteriorated, even if bought at a special price, your legal rights are not affected and you should complain first of all to the shop manager then, if no satisfaction is obtained, to your local Trading Standards Officer who you can locate through the Town Hall. It is often preferable, though, to write a nice letter, fully documented, with a sample, to the Managing Director of the company concerned who will often, for the sake of goodwill (and most of the food companies are very jealous of their good reputation), refund your cost and may even give you something extra besides. However, if you are on the make, beware, because most manufacturers keep very accurate records of complainants and get wise to the person who frequently finds a dead mouse in the meat pie.

Foods for special nutritional purposes are subject to the provisions of an EEC Directive which strictly controls all claims and declarations in respect of infant, diabetic, slimming and other foods which make them appear that they are for a group of people with special nutritional needs. There is a problem in that some excellent foods which have a nutritional purpose may not, in the future, be able to declare it without a Medicines Licence! For example, a bran based breakfast cereal may not be able to say that it helps prevent constipation even though the Roman Army almost 2,000 years ago had to eat wholemeal bread to keep them free of constipation and no serious authority has doubted the benefits of bran ever since. Too often we are seeing legislation which is designed for consumer protection which effectively shields the consumer from the information needed to make an informed decision. It should surely be sufficient that advertising is decent, honest and truthful.

Hyperactivity in Children

Hyperactive children bring much strain and exhaustion to parents who have to manage offspring that sleep only a few hours out of twenty-four, may suffer from eczema and asthma and can not be calmed down.

As they grow older they become even more active and can easily become hurt. Difficulties are experienced with speech, balance and learning even if the IQ is high. They suffer from excessive thirst and often are prone to respiratory difficulties.

It was to help such parents and children that the Hyperactive Children's Support Group was formed in 1977. It is now a registered charity. The Secretary is Mrs Sally Bunday, 59 Meadowside, Angmering, West Sussex, BN16 4BW. (Please enclose an S.A.E.)

The Group recommends that parents try a diet based on the work of the American doctor, Ben Feingold. First, this means cutting out all food and drink containing synthetic colours or flavours, avoiding glutamates, nitrites, nitrates, BHA, BHT and benzoic acid. Second, for the first four to six weeks, foods containing natural salicylates (like aspirin chemically) should be avoided and then re-introduced *one at a time* to see if they cause problems. Such foods include almonds, apples, apricots, peaches, plums, prunes, oranges, tomatoes, tangerines, cucumbers, most soft fruits, cherries, grapes and raisins.

The 'E' numbers of additives that the HACSG recommend should be avoided are:

E102   Tartrazine   E110   Sunset Yellow FCF

E104	Quinoline Yellow	E120	Cochineal
107	Yellow 2G	E122	Carmoisine
E123	Amaranth	155	Brown HT
E124	Ponceau 4R	E210	Benzoic acid
E127	Erythrosine	E211	Sodium benzoate
128	Red 2G	E220	Sulphur dioxide
E132	Indigo Carmine	E250	Sodium nitrite
E133	Brilliant blue FCF	E251	Sodium nitrate
E150	Caramel	E320	Butylated hydroxyanisole
E151	Black PN	E321	Butylated hydroxytoluene
154	Brown FK		

Additives which are either dangerous to asthmatics or aspirin-sensitive people, and could reasonably be added to the HACSG listing or not allowed in food intended for babies or young children are:

E212 Potassium benzoate

E213 Calcium benzoate

E214 Ethyl 4-hydroxybenzoate

E215 Ethyl 4-hydroxybenzoate, sodium salt

E216 Propyl 4-hydroxybenzoate

E217 Propyl 4-hydroxybenzoate, sodium salt

E218 Methyl 4-hydroxybenzoate

E219 Methyl 4-hydroxybenzoate, sodium salt

E310 Propyl gallate

E311 Octyl gallate

E312 Dodecyl gallate

621 Sodium hydrogen L-glutamate

622 Potassium hydrogen L-glutamate

623 Calcium dihydrogen di-L-glutamate

627 Guanosine 5'-(*di*sodium phosphate)

631 Inosine 5'-(*di*sodium phosphate)

635 Sodium 5'-ribonucleotide

In *The Lancet* (Editorial, 20 March 1982, p. 662) the view was taken that most clinicians will say that the evidence 'does not yet justify prescribing the treatment, but does justify supporting families who have decided to try it themselves.'

The 'E' Number Categories

Permitted Colours (E100-E180)

Most colours are used for cosmetic reasons — to make the product look attractive. Quite a lot are natural in origin. For example, chlorophyll, the green colour of plants is the only permitted colour for sage cheese.

Some additional colours are being considered by the E.E.C. for an 'E' prefix, but the serial numbers which they have been allocated do not appear on food labels at the moment. These are 101a, 107, 128, 133, 154, 155.

The number of permitted colours is likely to be reduced as there is much dispute over the safety of quite a few — especially certain black, brown, yellow, green and red colours.

Some additional natural substances or extracts which also have a use as a colour are permitted but do not have E numbers. These include saffron, turmeric root, sandalwood and paprika. Citrus fruits can be marked with methyl violet.

Apart from marking, fresh meats, poultry, fish, fruits and vegetables may not be coloured. Neither can dried or condensed milk, tea and coffee.

Preservatives (E200-E290)

Preservatives are additives which check or prevent the growth of micro-organisms. Therefore from the point of view of providing safe food to the consumer at a point distant from the place of manufacture they constitute a group of substances which, on the whole, are far safer than mouldy food.

The ancient Greeks burnt sulphur over the wine in the cask before sealing, thus producing the preservative sulphur dioxide which is used in wines and many other foods to this day.

In the ideal world we would probably be better off with fresh, natural produce, but as things stand the moderate use of preservatives allows a variety in our diets which has benefits which may outweigh the risks. Such methods of preservation as alcohol, salting, adding sugar, smoking and adding herbs or spices are not included in this category.

Avoid preservatives only when you are sure that the food is fresh.

A number of the substances in the group have other functions, e.g., vinegars (acetic acids) are used for flavouring and carbon dioxide as a propellent in aerosols. Some of the additives are also classed as miscellaneous because they have additional functions. These include E260, E261, 262, E262 and E290.

Permitted Anti-oxidants (E300-E321)
The oxygen in the air causes many food products to undergo changes which make them unfit to eat causing, for example, rancidity in oils and fats.

The anti-oxidants vary from natural or nature-identical substances such as vitamin C (ascorbic acid) and vitamin E (the tocopherols) to others, the safety record of which is at least debatable such as E320, BHA and E321 BHT.

The amounts that may be used are controlled at various levels in different foodstuffs depending upon the amount needed to be effective.

Without anti-oxidants it would be impossible to provide many of the ready-packed foods on the supermarket shelves.

An additional anti-oxidant, ethoxyquin which does not have an 'E' number, is permitted for preserving apples and pears by being used as a surface spray to prevent 'scald'.

Emulsifiers and Stabilizers: Some numbers between E322 and 494.
When an egg is used to make a mayonnaise or to bind a sauce the lecithin in the egg works as an emulsifier. Lecithin is E322 which nowadays, for reasons of economy, is usually produced from soya beans.

Many of the emulsifiers and stabilizers are safe and natural.

The polyphosphates, E450, which are used to 'tenderize' many cured meats including ham are in reality a way of adding that low cost substance water. Frozen poultry often also has additions of polyphosphates enabling substantial increases in weight to be made.

In July 1979 the magazine of the Consumer Association, *Which?*, did a survey on cooked ham and found water added in percentages ranging from nil right up to 42 per cent in certain canned products. They found no relation between price and water content.

Two additives are permitted which do not have proposed or actual 'E' numbers and these are dioctyl sodium sulphosuccinate and the extract of Quillaia which is allowed in soft drinks.

Sweeteners (E420-421)

Only two of the permitted sweeteners have 'E' numbers, sorbitol and mannitol.

The regulations in the U.K. concerning permitted sweeteners were revised in 1983 when four exhaustively tested new sweeteners were added which are acesulfame potassium, aspartame, thaumatin and xylitol. Hydrogenated glucose syrup, isomalt and certain forms of saccharin are also listed as permitted sweeteners.

Other sweet substances are classed as foods rather than permitted sweeteners and these include sugar (sucrose), glucose (dextrose), fruit sugar (fructose) and milk sugar (lactose).

Solvents (E422)

Certain liquids which are not natural food substances are used to extract or dissolve foods so that they can be incorporated into products. A commonly used substance is alcohol in the form of ethyl alcohol or ethanol with which many flavouring and colouring extracts are made.

Other permitted solvents include ethyl acetate, ether, various glycerols (glycerol is the only solvent with an 'E' number). The other two which may be used are iso-propyl alcohol and propylene glycol.

Mineral Hydrocarbons (905-907)

Mineral hydrocarbons are used to prevent drying out of certain foods and as a polish to make foods shiny.

They are permitted in dried fruits, sugar confectionery, chewing sweets, cheese rind and eggs which must be marked 'sealed'.

Modified Starches (E1400-E1442)

These are to be found on certain products (we found E1422 on several dairy products such as milkshakes in the Summer of 1984) but it must be *emphasized emphatically* that these E numbers were proposals that were never accepted and are definitely *not* permissible to be used on packs in the U.K., even though there is no suggestion that they are not safe.

So that you know what you are getting if one of these numbers crops up, the full listing is as follows:

E1400	White or yellow dextrins, roasted starch.
E1401	Acid treated starches.
E1402	Alkaline treated starches.
E1403	Bleached starches.
E1404	Oxidised starches.
E1410	Mono starch phosphate.
E1411	Di starch phosphate. ⎫ produced in different ways.
E1412	Di starch phosphate. ⎭
E1413	Phosphated di starch phosphate.
E1414	Acetylated di starch phosphate.
E1420	Starch acetate. ⎫ produced in different ways.
E1421	Starch acetate. ⎭
E1422	Acetylated di starch adipate.
E1423	Acetylated di starch glycerol.
E1430	Di starch glycerol.
E1440	Hydroxypropyl starch.
E1441	Hydroxypropyl di starch glycerol.
E1442	Hydroxypropyl di starch phosphate.

Miscellaneous Additives (E170-927)

This group is not a numerical run between these two numbers. So many different substances with various purposes not covered by other regulations are incorporated in the Miscellaneous section that no useful guidance can be given that is not better found under the individual listing.

In this group is found substances like monosodium glutamate which is a flavour modifier or enhancer, propellant gases for food aerosols, bulking agents, anti-foaming substances, acids and glazing and releasing agents.

620, 622 and 623 are allowed in dietetic foods; 903 in chocolate and sugar confectionery; 353 in wine, 385 is allowable in canned fish and shellfish and brandy.

Certain additives (see text) are not permitted in baby and infant food and neither is 2-aminoethanol which may be used in peeled fruit and peeled vegetables so particular care needs to be taken when buying these to be sure that the substance is not included if they are to be eaten by little children.

Meat Products

Regulations governing meat products and spreadable fish products were laid before Parliament in October 1984. Like the E numbering provisions, these will come into full operation by July 1986.

Polyphosphates (E450) allow the manufacturer to add water to meat products without it becoming obvious to the consumer. If the meat is cooked or raw and contains added water, then the producer will have to declare: 'with not more than x per cent added water.' X is the maximum added water content of the food. On the other hand, if the meat is uncooked and cured, such as bacon, of which more than 10 per cent is added water, then the declaration has to say 'with not more than y per cent added water'; but that does *not* mean that this figure represents the amount of added water — y represents a multiple of 5 by which the percentage of water in the product exceeds 10 per cent! Finally, to make matters clear to our (presumably computer owning!) consumer — if it is cooked pure meat then the declaration has to say 'with not more than z per cent added water', z being an indication in multiples of 5 of the percentage of water added.

There is a list of parts of the carcass which may *not* be used in *uncooked* meat products — and may therefore be used in cooked meat products. You will be glad to know what comprehensive use manufacturers of cooked meat products can make of the slaughtered animal because they can use the brains, foot, large intestine, small intestine, lungs, oesophagus, rectum, spinal cord, spleen, stomach, testicles and udder. There has to be an argument for manufacturers to tell us just what parts of the animal are used and how much, not just the blanket description 'offal'.

A meat pie weighing between 100g and 200g must have a meat content of not less than 21 per cent of the total. If the pie weighs less than 100g the meat content can shrink to 19 per cent of the food, otherwise the meat content can soar to the dizzy heights of 25 per cent as a minimum *but*, of these percentages, the lean meat content need only be half so, at the worst, a quarter of a pound pork pie may contain just over a third of an ounce of lean meat — and it may include unexpected parts of the beast.

The true nature of the contents are then disguised in taste and appearance by the use of flavour enhancers, such as monosodium glutamate (number 621). It can then be coloured, flavoured and, after the addition of the appropriate amount of water, you can have, at the worst, a very fatty pie but one which looks and tastes good. Though of course there are many pie manufacturers who certainly do use the finest ingredients, it would be worth their while making clear claims. The fat content of burgers and sausages is also controlled, in general so that the fat content of the meat part of burgers does not exceed 35 per cent and of sausages, 50 per cent.

Many German meat products are labelled with their fat content. In order to be able to eat sensibly we should demand that such information be available throughout the E.E.C.

Permitted Colours

E100   **Curcumin (C.I. 75300)**

Origin   Extract of turmeric root.

Function   Orange-yellow colour for whole food, or surface
                  only.

Adverse   None known.
Effects

Typical   Savoury rice
Products   Curry powders
                  Margarine
                  Processed cheese

E101   Riboflavin (Lactoflavin; Vitamin B2)

Origin   Produced from yeast, or more usually synthetically. Occurs naturally in liver, kidneys, green vegetables, eggs and milk and a small amount is synthesized by bacteria in the large intestine.

Function   Yellow or orange-yellow colour; vitamin B_2.

Adverse Effects   Little riboflavin is stored in the body; excess of requirements is excreted in the urine. No toxic problems.

Typical Products   Processed cheeses

101(a)   Riboflavin – 5'-phosphate (Riboflavin – 5'-[Sodium phosphate])

Origin   Prepared by chemical action on riboflavine.

Function   Yellow colour; vitamin B_2.

Adverse Effects   None known.

Typical Products   Various sugar products
Jams

Under consideration by the E.E.C. for an 'E' prefix.

E102   Tartrazine (C.I. 19140)

Origin   Synthetic, an azo dye (see glossary).

Function   Yellow colour.

Adverse Effects   Susceptible people, especially those sensitive to aspirin, and asthmatics, are sensitive to tartrazine. Reactions include urticaria (skin rashes), rhinitis (hayfever), bronchospasm (breathing problems), blurred vision and purple patches on the skin. It has recently been suggested that tartrazine in fruit cordials may be responsible for wakefulness in small children at night. See also pages 12-14.

Typical Products
- Packet convenience foods
- Rind of cheese
- Smoked cod and haddock
- Chewing gum
- Sweets
- Lime and lemon squash
- Seafood dressing
- Mint sauce and jelly
- Packet dessert topping
- Tinned fruit pie filling
- Tinned processed peas
- Salad cream
- Prepacked cakes
- Marzipan
- Piccalilli
- Brown sauce
- Maple flavour syrup
- Fizzy drinks
- Shells of capsules

A very commonly used colour.

E104   **Quinoline Yellow (C.I. 47005)**

Origin   Synthetic 'coal tar' dye (see glossary).

Function   Dull yellow to greenish yellow colour.

Adverse   See pages 12-14.
Effects

Typical   Scotch eggs
Products   Smoked haddock

---

107   **Yellow 2G**

Origin   Synthetic 'coal tar' dye, and azo dye (see glossary).

Function   Food colour.

Adverse   Yellow 2G belongs to a group of chemical dyes
Effects   known as azo dyes. People who suffer from
asthma and those sensitive to aspirin may also
show an allergic reaction to this colour. See also
pages 12-14.

Typical   —
Products   Under consideration by
the E.E.C. for an 'E'
prefix.

E110　　　**Sunset Yellow FCF (C.I. 15985)**

Origin　　　Synthetic 'coal tar' dye, and azo dye (see glossary).

Function　　Yellow colour.

Adverse　　An azo dye to which some people have an allergic
Effects　　　reaction. Important risk of allergy especially in
　　　　　　people showing aspirin sensitivity, producing
　　　　　　urticaria (skin rash), angioedema (swelling of the
　　　　　　blood vessels), gastric upset and vomiting. See
　　　　　　also pages 12-14.

Typical　　　Hot chocolate mix
Products　　Packet soup
　　　　　　Sweets
　　　　　　Packet trifle mix
　　　　　　Yogurt whip
　　　　　　Packet sorbet mix
　　　　　　Orange jelly biscuits
　　　　　　Packet breadcrumbs
　　　　　　Packet cheese sauce
　　　　　　　mix
　　　　　　Orange squash
　　　　　　Marzipan
　　　　　　Swiss roll
　　　　　　Apricot jam
　　　　　　Lemon curd

24

E120   **Cochineal (Carmine of Cochineal; Carminic acid; C.I. 75470)**

Origin   Cochineal is the natural red colour from the egg
             yolks and the fatty parts of the dried female insect
             Dactilopius coccus (*Dactilopiidae*) a native of
             central America, and the Canary Islands. It
             contains about 10 per cent of carminic acid.
             Carmine is produced from cochineal, as its
             aluminium lake.

Function   Red colour.

Adverse   See pages 12-14.
Effects

Typical   Now used fairly rarely
Products   because of high cost,
                 but available as
                 cochineal food
                 colour for home
                 cooking. Largely
                 replaced by E124 in
                 manufacturing.

25

| E122 | **Carmoisine (Azorubine; C.I. 14720)** |

Origin Synthetic azo dye (see glossary).

Function Red colour.

Adverse Effects An azo dye, therefore producing adverse reactions in sensitive people, or people with aspirin allergy, or asthmatics. These reactions may include urticaria (skin rashes) or oedema (swelling). See also pages 12-14.

Typical Products
Packet soup mix
Blancmange
Packet breadcrumbs
Packet jellies
Sweets
Packet cheesecake mix
Brown sauce
Savoury convenience
   food mix
Prepacked Swiss roll
Prepacked sponge
   pudding
Marzipan

| E123 | **Amaranth (C.I. 16185)** |

Origin Synthetic 'coal tar' dye and azo dye (see glossary).

Function Red colour.

Adverse Effects An azo dye, therefore to be avoided by people with aspirin sensitivity as it may cause urticaria (skin rash). See pages 12-14.

26

Typical *Products*	Packet soup
	Packet cake mix
	Packet trifle mix
	Liquid vitamin C
	preparations
	Gravy granules
	Tinned fruit pie fillings
	Quick setting jelly mix

E124   Ponceau 4R (C.I. 16255)

Origin   Synthetic 'coal tar' dye, and azo dye (see glossary).

Function   Red colour.

Adverse *Effects*   An azo dye, so should be avoided by people with aspirin sensitivity, and asthmatics. See pages 12-14.

Typical *Products*	Packet trifle mix
	Packet cheesecake mix
	Packet cake mix
	Packet soup
	Seafood dressing
	Dessert topping
	Tinned strawberries
	Tinned cherry,
	redcurrant and
	raspberry pie fillings
	Quick setting jelly mix

E127   **Erythrosine (C.I. 45430)**

Origin   Synthetic 'coal tar' dye (see glossary).

Function   Red colour. Also used in disclosing tablets for
                  revealing plaque on teeth.

Adverse   Can cause photoxicity (sensitivity to light). See
Effects   also pages 12-14.
                     Erythrosine contains 577mg of iodine per gram
                  and consumption of considerable amounts of
                  foods containing erythrosine could increase the
                  circulating thyroid-hormone to levels high
                  enough to cause hyperthyroidism (overactive
                  thryoid).

Typical   Glacé cherries
Products   Scotch eggs
                  Tinned red cherries,
                     strawberries and
                     rhubarb
                  Packet trifle mix
                  Quick custard mix
                  Biscuits
                  Prepacked Swiss roll

---

128   **Red 2G (C.I. 18050)**

Origin   Synthetic 'coal tar' dye, and azo dye (see glossary).

Function   Red colour.

Adverse Effects   Further toxicological studies required. See pages 12-14.

Typical Products   Sausages
Cooked meat products

Under consideration by
the E.E.C. for an 'E'
prefix.

E131   **Patent Blue V (C.I. 42051)**

Origin   Synthetic 'coal tar' dye (see glossary).

Function   Dark bluish-violet colour and diagnostic agent, used to colour the lymph vessels.

Adverse Effects   To be avoided by patients with a history of allergy. Allergic reactions may occur immediately or after a few minutes. They consist of skin sensitivity, itching and urticaria (nettle rash). More severe reactions, including shock and breathing problems, occur rarely. Nausea, low blood-pressure and tremor have been reported. See also pages 12-14.

Typical Products   Scotch eggs

E132   **Indigo Carmine (Indigotine; C.I. 73015)**

Origin   Synthetic 'coal tar' dye (see glossary).

Function   Blue colour and diagnostic agent (used to test whether the kidneys are functioning normally by producing blue urine after Indigo Carmine is injected into veins or muscles).

Adverse Effects   People with a history of allergy should avoid this colour. May cause nausea, vomiting, high blood-pressure, hypertension and occasionally allergic reactions such as skin rash, pruritus (itching) and breathing problems. See also pages 12-14.

Typical Products   Blancmange
Biscuits
Sweets
Savoury convenience
     food mix

133   **Brilliant Blue FCF (C.I. 42090)**

Origin   Synthetic 'coal tar' dye (see glossary).

Function   Blue colour which can produce green hues in combination with tartrazine.

Adverse Effects   See pages 12-14.

Typical Products   Tinned processed peas

Under consideration by
     the E.E.C. for an 'E'
     prefix.

E140 **Chlorophyll (C.I. 75810)**

Origin Pure chlorophyll is not easy to isolate and the chlorophyll which is commercially available contains other plant pigments, fatty acids and phosphatides, and is known as 'technical chlorophyll'. The usual sources are nettles, grass and lucerne.

Function Food colour (green) and for medicines.

Adverse Effects None known.

Typical Products Fats
Oils
Soaps
Naturally green
vegetables and fruits
preserved in a liquid

E141 **Copper complexes of Chlorophyll and Chlorophyllins (C.I. 75810; Copper phaeophytins)**

Origin Derived from chlorophyll by substitution of groups of atoms within the chlorophyll molecule.

Function The copper complexes are olive-green oil-soluble colours; the chlorophyllins are green water-soluble colours.

Adverse Effects None known.

Typical Products Green vegetables and
fruits preserved in a
liquid

E142   **Green S (Acid Brilliant Green BS; Lissamine Green; C.I. 44090)**

Origin   Synthetic 'coal tar' dye (see glossary).

Function   Green colour.

*Adverse   None known.
Effects*

---

*Typical   Packet cheesecake mix
Products*   Tinned peas
               Packet breadcrumbs
               Gravy granules
               Mint jelly and sauce

E150 **Caramel**

Origin By the action of heat or chemicals on carbohydrates.

Function Brown colour; flavouring agent.

Adverse Effects The safety of caramel has long been questioned. The number of types now available has been reduced to six to meet all the needs of the food industry and work is being carried out to find the safest form. Caramel produced with ammonia has been shown to cause vitamin B_6 deficiency in rats. (Spector and Huntoon, *Toxicology and Appl. Pharm.*, 62, 172-178, 1982. *Nutrition Bulletin* 1982.)

Typical Products Chocolate dessert whip
Oyster sauce
Biscuits
Packet soup
Sachet marinade
Tinned sauce
Scotch eggs
Packet cake mix
Savoury convenience
    food mix
Sweet pickle
Pickled onions
Gravy granules
Mint jelly
Prepacked cakes
Soya sauce
Fruit sauce

E151   **Black PN (Brilliant Black BN; C.I. 28440)**

Origin   Synthetic 'coal tar' dye, and azo dye (see glossary).

Function   Black colour.

Adverse Effects   Intestinal cysts were found in pigs given black PN in a 90-day feeding study. Further studies required. See also pages 12-14.

Typical Products   Blackcurrant
    cheesecake mix
Brown sauce

E153   **Carbon Black (Vegetable Carbon)**

Origin   Natural — from burning of plant material.

Function   Black colour.

Adverse Effects   Probably few risks when the method of manufacture is perfected and a plentiful supply of oxygen is available for the combustion, but in the United States it is banned in the belief that it may be implicated in causing cancer.

Typical Products   Concentrated fruit
    juices
Jams
Jellies

154   Brown FK (Kipper Brown; Food Brown)

Origin   Synthetic mixture of azo dyes (see glossary).

Function   Brown colour, especially for kippers.

Adverse   Experiments with bacteria have shown that two
Effects   of the colour's constituents cause genetic
                mutation. See also pages 12-14.

Typical   Kippers
Products   Smoked mackerel

                Under consideration by
                    the E.E.C. for an 'E'
                    prefix

---

155   Brown HT (C.I. 20285; Chocolate brown HT)

Origin   Synthetic 'coal tar' dye and azo dye (see glossary).

Function   Brown colour.

Adverse   An azo dye, therefore to be avoided by people
Effects   with asthma, aspirin sensitivity and skin
                sensitivity. See also pages 12-14.

Typical   —
Products
                Under consideration by
                    the EEC for an 'E'
                    prefix.

E160(a)	**alpha-carotene, beta-carotene, gamma-carotene (C.I. 75130)**

Origin — Extracts of natural plant pigments found especially in carrots, green leafy vegetables, tomatoes, apricots, rosehips and oranges.

Function — Orange-yellow colour; becomes vitamin A in the body.

Adverse Effects — None known.

Typical Products
Soft margarine
Butter/margarine
Yogurt dessert whip
Prepacked coffee
 sponge cake
Sandwich cake

E160(b)	**Annatto, Bixin, Norbixin (C.I. 75120)**

Origin — A vegetable dye from the seed coats of the tropical Annatto tree (*Bixa orellana*).

Function — Yellow to peach colour.

Adverse Effects — None known.

Typical Products	Margarine
	Cheshire cheese
	Butter — especially to
	    darken pale-coloured
	    butter produced in
	    the winter
	Frying oil
	Carton coleslaw
	Prepacked sponge
	    pudding

E160(c)   Capsanthin (Capsorubin)

Origin   Natural extract from paprika.

Function   Flavouring; orange colour.

Adverse Effects   None known.

Typical Products   Processed cheese slices

E160(d)   Lycopene (C.I. 75125)

Origin   Natural plant extract from tomatoes.

Function   Red colour.

Adverse Effects   None known.

Typical Products   —

E160(e)   **beta-apo-8'-carotenal (C_{30}) (beta-8'-apocarotenal)**

Origin   Natural plant derivative.

Function   Orange to yellowish red colour.

Adverse Effects   None known.

Typical Products   —

E160(f)   **Ethyl ester of beta apo-8'-carotenoic acid (C_{30})**

Origin   Natural plant derivative.

Function   Natural orange to yellow colour.

Adverse Effects   None known.

Typical Products   —

E161   **Xanthophylls**
E161(a)   **Flavoxanthin (C.I. 75135)**

Origin   A carotenoid pigment. Carotene is one of the
                  plant pigments of green leaves isolated from a
                  species of buttercup (*Ranunculus acris*).

Function   Yellow colour.

Adverse   None known.
Effects

Typical   —
Products

E161   **Xanthophylls**
E161(b)   **Lutein (C.I. 75135)**

Origin   Related to carotene, one of the plant pigments
                  present in abundance in green leaves. Also present
                  in egg yolks.

Function   Yellow to reddish colour.

Adverse   None known.
Effects

Typical   —
Products

E161   **Xanthophylls**
E161(c)   **Cryptoxanthin (C.I. 75135)**

Origin   Related to carotene, part of the green plant pigment chlorophyll, especially well represented in the petals and berries of the *Physalis* (Bladder Cherry, Cape Gooseberry) genus (*Solanaceae*, the potato and tomato family) and also present in orange rind, egg yolk and butter.

Function   Yellow colour.

Adverse Effects   None known.

Typical Products   —

E161   **Xanthophylls**
E161(d)   **Rubixanthin (C.I. 75135)**

Origin   Related to carotene, especially present in rosehips.

Function   Yellow colour.

Adverse Effects   None known.

Typical Products   —

E161   **Xanthophylls**
E161(e)   **Violoxanthin (C.I. 75135)**

Origin   Natural extract from the plant pigment carotene, especially isolated from yellow pansies (*Viola tricolor*).

Function   Yellow colour.

Adverse   None known.
Effects

Typical   —
Products

E161   **Xanthophylls**
E161(f)   **Rhodoxanthin (C.I. 75135)**

Origin   A naturally occurring carotenoid pigment found in small amounts only in, for example, the seeds of the Yew tree (*Taxus baccata*).

Function   Yellow colour.

Adverse   None known.
Effects

Typical   —
Products

| E161 | **Xanthophylls** |
| E161(g) | **Canthaxanthin (C.I. 75135)** |

Origin	A widely-distributed carotenoid pigment which can be isolated from some mushrooms and flamingo feathers.
Function	Natural orange colour.
Adverse Effects	None known.

Typical Products	Mallow biscuits
	'Sun-tan' capsules
	    which when taken
	    make the skin yellow
	    simulating a tan but
	    without sun-
	    screening effect.

| E162 | **Beetroot Red (Betanin)** |

Origin	Natural extract of beetroot.
Function	Deep purplish-red colour.
Adverse Effects	None known.

Typical Products	Oxtail soup.

E163   **Anthocyanins (Schultz 1394 & 1400)**

Origin
Natural plant pigments — E163(a) Cyanidin (red); E163(b) Delphinidin (blue); E163(c) Malvidin (purple); E163(d) Pelargonidin (red brown); E163(e) Peonidin (dark red); E163(f) Petunidin (dark red). They are all red, blue or violet pigments which are present in the cell sap of many flowers, fruits, stems and leaves.

Function
Food colouring.

Adverse Effects
None known.

Typical Products
Sorbet mix

E170   **Calcium carbonate (Chalk; C.I. 77220)**

Origin
Naturally occurring mineral.

Function
Alkali, firming agent, release agent (in vitamin tablets), calcium supplements and surface food colourant.

Adverse Effects
None known.

Typical Products
Bread
Biscuits
Buns and cakes
Ice cream
Sweets
Vitamin and other
    tablets

E171   **Titanium dioxide (C.I. 77891)**

Origin   Prepared from the naturally occurring mineral
               ilmenite.

Function   White surface colour.

Adverse   None known.
Effects

Typical   Cottage cheese
Products   Vitamin tablets and
                   capsules
                Horseradish cream
                Horseradish sauce

E172   **Iron oxides, iron hydroxides (yellow/
               brown: C.I. 77492; red: 77491;
               brown: 77499)**

Origin   Naturally occurring pigments.

Function   Yellow, red, orange, brown and black colour.

Adverse   —
Effects

Typical   Salmon and shrimp
Products   paste
                Packet dessert mix
                Packet cake mix

44

E173   **Aluminium (C.I. 77000)**

Origin   Naturally occurring as the ore, bauxite.

Function   Metallic colour for surface only.

Adverse   Slight intestinal absorption of aluminium — any
Effects   absorbed is quickly excreted by healthy kidneys.

Typical   Solely for external
Products   covering of dragées
             and decoration of
             sugar-coated flour
             confectionery, silvery
             finish to pills and
             tablets.

E174   **Silver (C.I. 77820)**

Origin   Naturally occurring metal.

Function   Metallic surface colour.

Adverse   Silver salts are toxic to bacteria and lower life-
Effects   forms. Long, regular consumption can lead to
             argyria, a blue-grey skin, which is not dangerous.

Typical   Purely for dragées and
Products   sugar-coated flour
             confectionery.

E175   **Gold (C.I. 77480)**

Origin   Naturally occurring metal.

Function   Metallic surface colour.

Adverse   Chemically very inactive, therefore harmless, but
Effects   expensive.

Typical   External application to
Products   dragées and sugar-
                   coated flour
                   confectionery

E180   **Pigment Rubine (Lithol Rubine BK;
               C.I. 15850)**

Origin   Synthetic, an azo dye (see glossary).

Function   Reddish colour.

Adverse   None known.
Effects

Typical   Solely for colouring the
Products   rind of cheese

Preservatives

E200	**Sorbic acid**

Origin   Occurs naturally in some fruits. May be obtained from the berries of mountain ash (*Sorbus aucuparia*), and can be manufactured synthetically.
Products permitted to use E200 may also use the forms in E201, E202 and E203.

Function   Preservative, inhibiting the growth of yeasts and moulds.

Adverse Effects   Possible skin irritant.

Typical Products

Fermented milks
Yogurt
Gelatin capsules
Fruit salads
Sweets
Soft drinks
Bottled cheese spread
Processed cheese slices
Packet cake topping
Surface of cheese
Prepacked cake
Frozen pizza

Candied peel
Canned cauliflower
Wine and cider
Dessert sauces
Fillings and toppings
Soup concentrates

Limits of Use Generally 1000mg/kg.

E201	**Sodium sorbate**
Origin	Sodium salt of sorbic acid which occurs naturally or is manufactured synthetically.
Function	Preservative.
Adverse Effects	None known.
Typical Products	Frozen pizza

E202   **Potassium sorbate**

Origin   Prepared from sorbic acid with potassium hydroxide.

Function   Antifungal and antibacterial preservative, more soluble than sorbic acid.

Adverse Effects   None known.

Typical Products
Fermented milk
Yogurt
Margarine/butter spread
Cheese spread
Salad dressing
Glacé cherries
Frozen vanilla pudding
Seafood dressing
Prepacked cakes
Tinned fruit pie fillings
Frozen pizza

E203   **Calcium sorbate**

Origin   Synthetic.

Function   Antifungal and antibacterial preservative.

Adverse Effects   None known.

Typical Products
Fermented milk
    products
Yogurt

Typical Packet Soup (Vegetable)

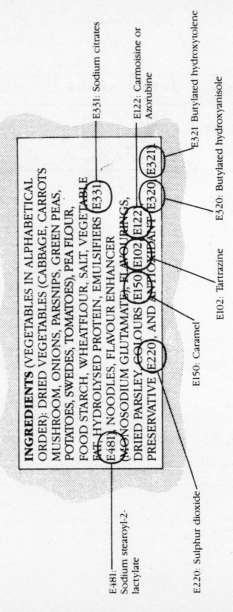

INGREDIENTS (VEGETABLES IN ALPHABETICAL ORDER): DRIED VEGETABLES (CABBAGE, CARROTS MUSHROOM, ONIONS, PARSNIPS, GREEN PEAS, POTATOES, SWEDES, TOMATOES), PEA FLOUR, FOOD STARCH, WHEATFLOUR, SALT, VEGETABLE FAT, HYDROLYSED PROTEIN, EMULSIFIERS (E481), NOODLES, FLAVOUR ENHANCER (MONOSODIUM GLUTAMATE), FLAVOURINGS, DRIED PARSLEY COLOURS (E150, E102, E122), AND ANTIOXIDANT (E220), PRESERVATIVE (E331).

E481: Sodium stearoyl-2-lactylate

E220: Sulphur dioxide

E331: Sodium citrates

E122: Carmoisine or Azorubine

E321 Butylated hydroxytolene

E321: Butylated hydroxyanisole

E320: Butylated hydroxytolene

E102: Tartrazine

E150: Caramel

50

Typical Packet Pork Sausages

INGREDIENTS: PORK, WATER, RUSK, STARCH, TURKEY,
SALT, SPICES, SOYA PROTEIN CONCENTRATE,
SODIUM POLYPHOSPHATE, HERBS, DEXTROSE,
FLAVOUR ENHANCER (MONOSODIUM GLUTAMATE),
ANTIOXIDANT (E301) (E304) (E307), SUGAR, PRESERVATIVE
(E223), FLAVOURING, COLOUR (E128)

E223: Sodium
metabisulphite

E128: Red 2G

E301: Sodium-L-
ascorbate

E307: Synthetic
alpha-tocopherol

E304: 6-0-Palmitoyl-
L-ascorbic acid

Typical Packet Sliced Meat Loaf (Turkey and Ham)

INGREDIENTS: CURED TURKEY (TURKEY, SALT,
PRESERVATIVE: (E250) HAM WITH PRESERVATIVE: (E250),
PORK, WATER, STARCH, CASEINATES, SPICES, SODIUM
POLYPHOSPHATE, HERBS, ANTIOXIDANT: (E301)
FLAVOUR ENHANCER: MONOSODIUM GLUTAMATE.

E250:
Sodium nitrite

E301: Sodium-L-
ascorbate

E250: Sodium
nitrite

51

E210   Benzoic acid

Origin   Occurs naturally in many edible berries but usually prepared synthetically.

Function   Preservatives — antibacterial and antifungal.

Adverse Effects   People who suffer from asthma or who have recurrent urticaria are likely to be sensitive to benzoic acid. It may also cause gastric irritation if consumed in large quantities. It has been reported to be responsible for neurological disorders and to react with the preservative sodium bisulphite (E222). See also pages 12-14.

Typical Products   Jams
Beer
Dessert sauces
Flavouring syrups
Fruit pulp and purée
Fruit juice
Marinated herring and
    mackerel
Pickles
Salad cream and
    dressing
Fruit yogurt
Coffee essence
Products permitted to
    use E210 may also
    use E211, E212 and
    E213.

| Limits | These vary between 120mg/kg in fruit yogurt to 160mg/kg in soft drinks, 250mg/kg in products such as olives, sauces, salad cream and pickles to 450mg/kg in coffee essence to 850mg/kg in Indonesian sambal oelek right up to 2000mg/kg in unfermented grape juice intended for the sacrament. |

E211 **Sodium benzoate**

Origin The sodium salt of benzoic acid.

Function Preservative — antibacterial and antifungal — effective only in slightly acid environment.

Adverse Effects People who suffer from asthma, or who have recurrent urticaria, may be sensitive to Sodium benzoate and exhibit allergic reactions. See pages 12-14.

Typical Products
Caviar
Prawns
Sweets
Margarine
Fruit pies
Soft drinks
Oyster sauce
Salad dressing
Barbecue sauce
Mexican taco sauce
Cheesecake mix
Soya sauce
Orange squash

E212 **Potassium benzoate**

Origin   The potassium salt of benzoic acid.

Function   Preservative — antibacterial and antifungal.

Adverse   People who suffer from asthma or are allergic to
Effects   aspirin or have recurrent urticaria, may be
             sensitive to potassium benzoate and show allergic
             reactions. See pages 12-14.

Typical   —
Products

E213 **Calcium benzoate**

Origin   The calcium salt of benzoic acid.

Function   Preservative — antibacterial and antifungal.

Adverse   People who suffer from asthma or recurrent
Effects   urticaria, or are allergic to aspirin, may be sensitive
             to calcium benzoate and exhibit allergic reactions.
             See pages 12-14.

Typical   —
Products

E214 **Ethyl 4-hydroxybenzoate (Ethyl *para*-hydroxybenzoate)**

Origin   Produced from benzoic acid.

Function   Preservative — antibacterial and antifungal.

Adverse Effects	Some people are hypersensitive to this substance, especially those sensitive to aspirin, asthmatics, those with recurrent urticaria. There may be skin sensitivity and/or a numbing effect on the mouth. See pages 12-14.

Typical Products

Cooked prepacked
   beetroot
Chicory and coffee
   essence
Dessert sauces
Flavouring syrups
Flavourings
Liquid foam headings
Freeze drinks
Fruit based pie fillings
Preserved fruit — glacé,
   crystallized or
   drained
Fruit pulp or purée
Fruit juices
Marinated mackerel or
   herring
Salad cream
Jam

Products permitted to
   use E214 may also
   use E215.

Limits

160mg/kg in freeze drinks.
250mg/kg in beetroot, pickles and salad cream.
800mg/kg in flavouring syrups, fruit-based pie fillings, fruit pulp, juices, and concentrated soft drinks.
1000mg/kg in preserved fruit, marinated fish.
10000mg/kg in foam headings.

E215   **Ethyl 4-hydroxybenzoate, sodium salt (Sodium ethyl *para*-hydroxybenzoate)**

Origin   Produced from benzoic acid.

Function   Preservative — antibacterial and antifungal.

Adverse Effects   Some people are allergic to this substance, especially those sensitive to aspirin, asthmatics, those with recurrent urticaria. There may be skin sensitivity and/or a numbing effect on the mouth. See pages 12-14.

Typical Products   —

E216   **Propyl 4-hydroxybenzoate (n-Propyl p-hydroxybenzoate; Propyl *para*-hydroxybenzoate)**

Origin   Produced from benzoic acid.

Function   Preservative — antimicrobial.

Adverse Effects   Skin sensitivity with a numbing effect on the mouth. See pages 12-14.

Typical
Products

Beer
Cooked prepacked
    beetroot
Coffee and chicory
    essence
Colouring matter in
    solution
Dessert sauces
Flavouring syrups
Freeze drinks
Fruit-based pie fillings
Crystallized, glacé or
    drained fruit
Fruit pulp or purée
Glucose and soft drinks
Marinated herring and
    mackerel
Pickles
Salad cream

Products permitted to
    use E216 may also
    use E217.

Limits

160mg/kg in freeze drinks.
250mg/kg in beetroot, pickles and salad cream.
800mg/kg in flavourings, fruit-based pie fillings,
    fruit pulp, juices and concentrated soft drinks.
1000mg/kg in preserved fruit and marinated fish.

E217	**Propyl 4-hydroxybenzoate, sodium salt (Sodium n-propyl p-hydroxybenzoate; Sodium propyl *para*-hydroxybenzoate)**

Origin   Produced from benzoic acid.

Function   Preservative — antimicrobial.

Adverse Effects   Allergic reactions to this substance may develop in asthmatics, those with recurrent urticaria or people sensitive to aspirin. There may be skin sensitivity and/or a numbing effect on the mouth. See pages 12-14.

Typical Products   —

E218	**Methyl 4-hydroxybenzoate (Methyl *para*-hydroxybenzoate)**

Origin   Synthetic.

Function   Preservative — antimicrobial agent.

Adverse Effects   Some people may exhibit allergic reactions to this substance mainly affecting the skin or mouth. See pages 12-14.

Typical
Products

Beer

Cooked prepacked
    beetroot

Coffee and chicory
    essence

Colouring matter in
    solution

Dessert sauces

Flavouring syrups

Freeze drinks

Fruit-based pie fillings

Crystallized, glacé or
    drained fruit

Fruit pulp or purée

Glucose and soft drinks

Marinated mackerel and
    herring

Pickles

Salad cream

Sauces

Snack meals

Soup concentrates

Products permitted to
    use E218 may also
    use E219.

Limits

160mg/kg in freeze drinks.

175mg/kg in snack meals and soup concentrates.

250mg/kg in beetroot, pickles and salad cream.

800mg/kg in flavourings, fruit-based pie fillings,
    fruit pulp, juices and concentrated soft drinks.

1000mg/kg in preserved fruit and marinated fish.

E219   **Methyl 4-hydroxybenzoate, sodium salt (Sodium methyl *para*-hydroxybenzoate; Sodium methyl hydroxybenzoate)**

Origin   Produced from benzoic acid.

Function   Preservative — active against fungi, and yeasts but less active against bacteria.

Adverse Effects   Allergic reactions have occurred when preparations containing hydroxybenzoates have been applied to the skin. Similar reactions have also occurred following intravenous or oral administration. Hydroxybenzoates have a numbing effect on the mouth. See pages 12-14.

Typical Products   —

E220   **Sulphur dioxide**

Origin   Occurs naturally but produced chemically by sulphur or gypsum combustion.

Function   Preservative; antioxidant; improving agent; bleaching agent (flour); vitamin C stabilizer.

Adverse Effects   Irritation of the alimentary food canal. Bleaching of flour has not been shown to be 100 per cent safe: it destroys much of the flour's vitamin E content. See also pages 12-14.

Typical
Products

Raspberry juice
Raspberry syrup
Fruit salads
Packet soup
Glacé cherries
Dried bananas and
    apricots
Blackcurrant jam
Desiccated coconut
Tinned cauliflower
Beer, wine, cider and
    cider vinegar
Candied peel
Tinned crabmeat
Fruit-based milk and
    cream desserts
Flavourings
Freeze drinks
Fruit-based pie fillings
Crystallized, glacé or
    drained fruit
Fruit pulp and purée
Fruit juices
Fruit spread
Powdered garlic
Gelatin
Dry root ginger
Glucose and soft drinks
Frozen mushrooms
Dehydrated vegetables
Sausage meat

Products permitted to
    contain E220 may
    also contain E221,
    E222, E223, E224
    and E227.

Limits	An astonishing range of additions are permitted, presumably calculated on the basis of the likely level of consumption, from 50mg/kg in desiccated coconut, 70mg/kg in beer through 100mg/kg in candied peel or canned cauliflower to 200mg/kg in cider, 2000mg/kg in most dried fruits right up to 30,000mg/kg in the dry enzyme from papaya, papain.

E221   **Sodium sulphite**

Origin	Synthetic.
Function	Preservative — antimicrobial; antioxidant in alkaline preparations. Main use is for 'fixing' photographs!
Adverse Effects	All sulphites may be dangerous to asthmatics.
Typical Products	Preserved egg yolk

E222   **Sodium hydrogen sulphite (Sodium bisulphite; acid sodium sulphite)**

Origin	Synthetic.
Function	Preservative; bleach.
Adverse Effects	A dose of 115mg per kilogram of body weight killed 50 per cent of a group of rats. All sulphites may be dangerous to asthmatics.

Typical
Products —

E223   **Sodium metabisulphite**
              (Diosodium pyrosulphite)

Origin   Synthetic.

Function   Preservative; anti-oxidant.

Adverse   Ingestion of sodium metabisulphite and other
Effects   sulphites may cause gastric irritation due to
              liberation of sulphurous acid. Treatment of foods
              with sulphites reduces their thiamine (Vitamin B_1)
              content, so foods that contain a significant source
              of thiamine — meat, cereals, dairy products —
              should not be treated. Known cause of food
              aversion and allergic skin reactions. All sulphites
              may be dangerous to asthmatics.

Typical   Orange squash
Products   Pickled onions
              Pickled red cabbage
              Carton salad
              Packet mashed potatoes

E224   Potassium metabisulphite (Potassium pyrosulphite)

Origin   Synthetic.

Function   Preservative, especially in the Campden process for preserving fruit and home-made wine. Used to stop fermentation in breweries.

Adverse Effects   Evidence in the United States indicates that asthmatics may be sulphite-sensitive. Some asthmatics have experienced wheezing, dyspnea (difficulty in breathing), cyanosis (deoxygenation of the blood), faintness and even unconsciousness after exposure to common sulphiting agents like potassium metabisulphite.

Typical Products   Campden tablets

E226   **Calcium sulphite**

Origin   Synthetic.

Function   Preservative; firming agent.

Adverse   Ingestion of sulphite may cause gastric irritation
Effects   due to the liberation of sulphurous acid.
                Treatment of foods with sulphite reduces their
                thiamine (vitamin B_1) content, so foods
                containing a significant source of thiamine (meat,
                cereals, dairy products) should not be treated. All
                sulphites may be dangerous to asthmatics.

Typical   Cider
Products

E227   **Calcium hydrogen sulphite**
                (Calcium bisulphite)

Origin   Synthetic.

Function   Preservative; prevents secondary fermentation;
                firming agent.

Adverse   Ingestion of sulphites may cause gastric irritation
Effects   due to the liberation of sulphurous acid.
                Treatment of foods with sulphites reduces their
                thiamine (vitamin B_1) content, and may
                contribute to a vitamin deficiency. All sulphites
                may be dangerous to asthmatics.

Typical   Beer
Products

E230 Biphenyl (Diphenyl)

Origin Synthetic, produced by action of heat on benzene.

Function Preservative — antifungal.
Inhibits the growth of species of *Pencillium* which cause citrus fruits to decay. Can penetrate the skin of fruit and might be included in food or drink prepared from fruit.

Adverse Effects Workers exposed to diphenyl reported nausea, vomiting and irritation to eyes and nose.

Typical Products Treatment of skins of oranges, lemons, grapefruit etc.
Can be partly removed with detergent. Rinse thoroughly afterwards.
Products permitted to use E230 may also use E231 and E232.

E231 2-Hydroxybiphenyl (o-Phenyl phenol; Orthophenylphenol)

Origin Synthetic, a substance used in the manufacture of rubber.

Function Preservative — antibacterial and antifungal.

Adverse Effects Workers exposed to biphenyl (diphenyl) reported nausea, vomiting and irritation to eyes and nose.

Typical	Surfaces of citrus fruits
Products	and treatment of
	paper in which they
	are wrapped.

Products permitted to
use E231 may also
use E230 and E232.

E232   **Sodium biphenyl-2-yl oxide**
(Sodium O-phenylphenol;
Sodium orthophenylphenate)

Origin   Synthetic (with a strong smell of soap).

Function   Preservative — antifungal.

Adverse   Alternative form of E231. Workers exposed to
Effects   biphenyl (diphenyl) reported nausea, vomiting,
and irritation to eyes and nose.

Typical   Penetration of the
Products   surface of citrus
fruits may cause the
substance to be
present in
marmalades and jams
produced from the
fruit.
Surface of citrus fruits
and paper used to
wrap citrus fruits.

E233   **2-(Thiazol-4-yl) benzimidazole (Thiabendazole)**

Origin   Synthetic.

Function   Preservative — fungicide.

Adverse   None known.
Effects

Typical   Treatment of the skins
Products   of citrus fruits and
   impregnating the
   paper in which they
   are wrapped.

---

234   **Nisin**

Origin   A polypeptide antibiotic substance produced by the growth of a bacterium called *Streptococcus lactis*. Several strains of cheese starter organisms produce nisin.

Function   Preservative.

Adverse   None known.
Effects

Typical   Cheese
Products   Clotted cream
   Cottage cheese
   Canned foods

   Under consideration by
      the E.E.C. for an 'E'
      prefix.

E236   **Formic acid**

Origin   Occurs naturally in the bodies of ants; produced
                  synthetically.

Function   Preservative — antibacterial action.

Adverse   Very caustic to the skin and if absorbed has been
Effects   known to cause urine disorders. Formic acid was
                  formerly used as a diuretic.

Typical   —
Products
                  Not permitted in the
                    U.K.

E237   **Sodium formate**

Origin   The sodium salt manufactured from formic acid.

Function   Preservative.

Adverse   Has diuretic properties and was formerly used
Effects   for this purpose.

Typical   —
Products
                  Not permitted in the
                    U.K.

E238   **Calcium formate**

Origin   The calcium salt of formic acid.

Function   Preservative.

Adverse   Has diuretic properties and was formerly used
Effects   for this purpose.

Typical   —
Products

      Not permitted in the
      U.K.

E239   **Hexamine (Hexamethylenetetramine)**

Origin   Synthetic, a derivative of benzene.

Function   Preservative — fungicide.

Adverse   Gastro-intestinal upsets may result from
Effects   prolonged use of hexamine by the production
      of formaldehyde. In addition, the urinary system
      may be affected and less frequently, skin rashes
      may occur. In experiments with animals,
      hexamine caused gene mutation and is suspected
      of being carcinogenic.

Typical   Marinated herrings and
Products   mackerel
      Provolone cheese

Limits   25mg/kg (expressed as formaldehyde)

E249   **Potassium nitrite**

Origin   Naturally occurring.

Function   Food preservative, curing agent.

Adverse Effects   Should not be used in food for babies under six months. Destroys red blood corpuscles. Reacts with amines to form nitrosamines which have been shown to be potentially carcinogenic. Preservatives in sausages have been linked with asthma.

Typical Products   Cooked meats
Sausages

Sodium nitrite (E250)
          may be used instead.

E250 Sodium nitrite

Origin Not naturally occurring; derived from sodium nitrate by chemical or bacterial action.

Function Food preservative (inhibiting the growth of *Clostridium botulinum* the bacterium responsible for botulism); curing salt.

Adverse Effects Nitrites may cause nausea and vomiting, dizziness, headaches, de-oxygenation of the blood, low blood pressure and collapse of the circulatory system. Nitrites form minute traces of nitrosamines in the stomach and these have been shown to be carcinogenic in animals but not yet in man. They are prohibited for sale in foods for babies and young children. Preservatives in sausages were shown to be responsible for asthma in a 57-year-old woman. See also pages 12-14.

Typical Products
Cured meat and cured
    meat products
Salted meat to fix the
    red colour
Pork sausage
Packet bacon steaks
Turkey and ham loaf
Smoked frankfurters
Bacon
Ham
Tongue
Pressed meat
Tinned meat
Frozen pizza

Limits (E250 and E251) 50mg/kg in cheese other than Cheddar, Cheshire or soft cheeses (of which only 5mg may be E250) 150mg/kg in cured meat (of which not more than 50mg may be E250) 400mg/kg in salami and similar acidified or fermented meat products (of which not more than 50mg may be E250) 500mg/kg in uncooked bacon and ham and cooked unsealed bacon and ham (of which not more than 200mg may be E250).

E251 **Sodium nitrate (Chile saltpetre)**

Origin Naturally occurring mineral (especially in the Atacama desert, Chile).

Function Preservative; curing salt.

Adverse Effects Nitrates are capable of being converted to nitrites either when food spoils or by bacteria in the stomach (especially in tiny babies). Nitrites can cause deoxygenation of the blood or form minute amounts of nitrosamines which may be carcinogenic. See also pages 12-14.

Typical Products Bacon
Pressed meats
Ham
Tongue
Beef
Canned meat
Cheese
Frozen pizza

Potassium nitrate (E252)
  may be used instead.

73

E252   **Potassium nitrate (Saltpetre)**

Origin   Naturally occurring mineral, or artificially
                  manufactured from waste animal and vegetable
                  material.

Function   Food preservative, curing salt, one of the oldest
                  and most effective ways of preserving meats.

Adverse   Gastro-enteritis with severe abdominal pain,
Effects   vomiting, vertigo, muscular weakness, and
                  irregular pulse can occur. Potassium nitrate may
                  be reduced to potassium nitrite in the gut by
                  bacterial action and this once absorbed can affect
                  the haemoglobin in the red blood corpuscles
                  preventing it carrying oxygen. Nitrites can
                  produce minute amounts of nitrosamines which
                  may be carcinogenic in man. Nevertheless
                  without the nitrates and nitrites there would be
                  many deaths from the growth of toxic micro-
                  organisms in meats.

Typical   Cured meats
Products   Sausages
                  Smoked frankfurters
                  Bacon, ham, tongue
                  Pressed meats
                  Tinned meats

E260   Acetic acid

Origin

Manufactured by the destructive distillation of wood. The acetic acid in vinegar is formed by the action of the bacterium *Acetobacter* on the alcohol in beer for malt vinegar or cider or wine for those vinegars.

Function

Antibacterial and at 5 per cent concentration may be bactericidal; substance permitted to stabilize the acidity of food; diluent for colouring matter.

Adverse Effects

No toxicological problems are known.

Typical Products

Foods which may
   provide a suitable
   environment for
   certain bacteria
Pickles
Chutneys
Cheese
Salad cream
Fruit sauce
Brown sauce
Spicy brown sauce
Mint sauce and jelly
Horseradish cream
Dilute acetic acid at
   about 5 per cent is
   called 'non-brewed
   condiment'

Typical Powdered Orange Drink

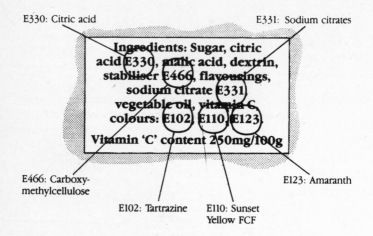

E330: Citric acid

E331: Sodium citrates

Ingredients: Sugar, citric acid E330, malic acid, dextrin, stabiliser E466, flavourings, sodium citrate E331 vegetable oil, vitamin C, colours: E102, E110, E123.

Vitamin 'C' content 250mg/100g

E466: Carboxy-methylcellulose

E123: Amaranth

E102: Tartrazine

E110: Sunset Yellow FCF

Typical Cartonned Orange Drink

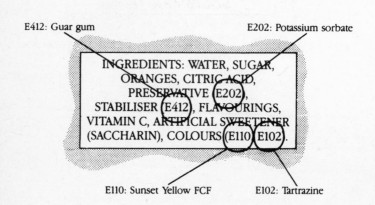

E412: Guar gum

E202: Potassium sorbate

INGREDIENTS: WATER, SUGAR, ORANGES, CITRIC ACID, PRESERVATIVE E202, STABILISER E412, FLAVOURINGS, VITAMIN C, ARTIFICIAL SWEETENER (SACCHARIN), COLOURS E110 E102.

E110: Sunset Yellow FCF

E102: Tartrazine

Typical Frothy Milk Shake (Strawberry)

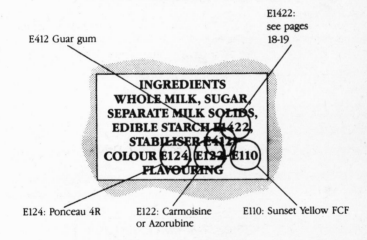

E412 Guar gum

E1422:
see pages
18-19

INGREDIENTS
WHOLE MILK, SUGAR
SEPARATE MILK SOLIDS,
EDIBLE STARCH E1422,
STABILISER E412,
COLOUR E124, E122, E110
FLAVOURING

E124: Ponceau 4R

E122: Carmoisine
or Azorubine

E110: Sunset Yellow FCF

E261 **Potassium acetate**

Origin   The potassium salt of acetic acid, E260.

Function   To preserve natural colour of plant and animal tissues; buffer.

Adverse   Potassium salts, taken by mouth in healthy people
Effects   cause little toxicity since potassium is rapidly excreted in the urine, but should be avoided by people with impaired kidneys.

Typical   —
Products

E262 **Sodium hydrogen diacetate (Sodium diacetate)**

Origin   Synthetic.

Function   Preservative — antimicrobial inhibitor especially against the spores of *Bacillus mesentericus* and *B. subtilis*. These spores are heat-resistant, and if present in bread and permitted to germinate, convert the bread into sticky yellow patches, which are capable of being pulled into long threads, hence the term 'rope-forming' micro-organisms.

Adverse   None known.
Effects

Typical   Bread
Products   Shaped crisps

262   Sodium acetate (anhydrous) and Sodium acetate

Origin   The sodium salt of acetic acid, E260.

Function   Buffer (acid or alkaline stabilizer).

Adverse Effects   Too much sodium in the body could be dangerous in babies and young children by increasing the body fluid salt concentrations either within or between the cells.

Typical Products   —

Under consideration by the E.E.C. for an 'E' prefix.

E263   Calcium acetate

Origin   The calcium salt of acetic acid, E260.

Function   Food preservative, preventing mould growth; sequestrant; firming agent.

Adverse Effects   None known.

Typical Products   Packet cheesecake mix
Quick setting jelly mix

E270 **Lactic acid**

Origin   Naturally occurring substance, produced by milk-souring organisms, also manufactured by fermentation of a carbohydrate with *Bacillus acidilactic* at high temperatures.

Function   Food preservative; capable of increasing the antioxidant effect of other substances; acid and flavouring.

Adverse   Could cause problems in very young or
Effects   premature babies who may have difficulty metabolizing it. No toxicological problems with adults.

Typical   Soft margarine
Products   Carbonated drinks
        Infant milks
        Confectionery
        Carton salad in dressing
        Salad dressing
        Pickled red cabbage
        Bottled cheese spread
        Sauce tartare

E280   **Propionic acid**

Origin   A naturally occurring fatty acid, one of the
products of digestion of cellulose by the gut-
inhabiting bacteria of herbivorous animals.
Produced by fermentation for commercial use.

Function   Food preservative — antifungal agent against
three families of fungi.

Adverse   No known toxicological problems.
Effects

Typical   Baking and dairy
Products   products
Pizza
Christmas puddings

Substances permitted to
use E280 may also
use E281, E282 and
E283.

Limit   300mg/kg (calculated on the weight of flour)

E281   Sodium propionate

Origin   The sodium salt of propionic acid.

Function   Food preservative — an antifungal agent against three families of moulds.

Adverse Effects   One report suggests that sodium propionate is involved with certain migraine headaches.

Typical Products   Dairy and bakery products

E282   Calcium propionate

Origin   Occurs naturally in Swiss cheese; prepared commercially from propionic acid.

Function   Preservative — antimicrobial mould inhibitor, especially 'rope' micro-organisms, which occur in bread. The spores of *Bacillus mesentericus* and *B. subtilis* are heat resistant and if present in bread and permitted to germinate convert the bread into sticky yellow patches, which are capable of being pulled into long threads.

Adverse Effects   No known toxicological problems.

Typical Products   Dairy and baking products
Frozen pizza

E283   **Potassium propionate**

Origin   The potassium salt of propionic acid.

Function   Preservative — mould inhibitor.

Adverse Effects   None known.

Typical Products   Dairy and bakery
       products
Christmas puddings

E290   **Carbon dioxide**

Origin   Natural gas, present in atmospheric air but produced by fermentation or the action of acid on a carbonate or as a by-product in the manufacture of lime.

Function   Preservative; coolant; freezant (liquid form); packaging gas.

Adverse Effects   Some carbonates in the stomach increase the secretion of gastric acid and promote absorption of liquid by the mucous membranes, increasing the effect of alcohol.

Typical Products   Fizzy and effervescent
       drinks

---

296   **Malic acid (DL-or-L-)**

Origin   L form present in apples, pears and many other temperate fruits. DL form produced chemically.

Function   Acid, flavouring.

Adverse   None known.
Effects

Typical   Tinned oxtail soup
Products   Shaped crisps
             Low calorie orange
                squash
             Packet spaghetti sauce
                mix

             Under consideration by
                the E.E.C. for an 'E'
                prefix.

---

297   Fumaric acid

Origin   A naturally occurring organic acid especially important in cell respiration. Prepared by fermentation for commercial use.

Function   Acidifier and flavouring agent; raising agent and antioxidant in baked goods.

Adverse Effects   None known.

Typical Products   Packet cheesecake mix
Yogurt whip

Under consideration by
   the E.E.C. for an 'E'
   prefix.

Permitted Anti-Oxidants

E300   **L-Ascorbic acid (Vitamin C)**

Origin   Naturally occurring substance in many fresh fruits
                  and vegetables; also manufactured by biological
                  synthesis.

Function   Vitamin C; antioxidant in emulsions of fats and
                  oils and in iron mixtures; browning inhibitor in
                  unprocessed cut fruits, fruit pulp and juices;
                  improving agent for flour; meat colour
                  preservative.

Adverse   Usually well tolerated. Large doses may cause
Effects   diarrhoea and/or dental erosion. More than 10g
                  per day could result in kidney stones in suscept-
                  ible people.

Typical
Products

Concentrated fruit
    drinks
Beer
Soft and fizzy drinks
Frozen egg products
Powdered and
    concentrated milk
Fruit jams and
    preserves
Frozen croquette
    potatoes
Dried potatoes (where
    its presence is
    desirable as a
    replacement for the
    vitamin C lost in
    processing.)

E301

**Sodium L-ascorbate (Vitamin C;
Sodium L-(+)-ascorbate)**

Origin

Prepared synthetically, the sodium salt of ascorbic
acid.

Function

Vitamin C; antioxidant; colour preservative.

Adverse
Effects

No toxicological problems in standard doses.

Typical
Products

Scotch eggs
Sausages
Turkey and ham loaf
Smoked frankfurters

E302　　**Calcium L-ascorbate**
　　　　　　(Calcium ascorbate)

Origin　　　Prepared synthetically.

Function　　Vitamin C; antioxidant; meat colour preservative.

Adverse　　None known.
Effects

Typical　　Scotch eggs
Products

E304　　**6-0-Palmitoyl-L-ascorbic acid**
　　　　　　(Ascorbyl palmitate)

Origin　　　Synthetic.

Function　　Antioxidant; colour preservative.

Adverse　　None known.
Effects

Typical　　Scotch eggs
Products　　Sausages
　　　　　　Chicken stock tablets

E306 **Extracts of natural origin rich in tocopherols (Vitamin E)**

Origin Extract of soya bean oil, wheat germ, rice germ, cottonseed, maize and green leaves, distilled in a vacuum.

Function Vitamin; antioxidant.

Adverse Effects None known in food use.

Typical Products Packet dessert topping
Vegetable oils

E307 **Synthetic *alpha*-tocopherol (Vitamin E; DL-*alpha*-tocopherol)**

Origin Synthetic.

Function Antioxidant; vitamin.

Adverse Effects None known in food use.

Typical Products Sausages

E308   **Synthetic *gamma*-tocopherol
(Vitamin E; DL-*gamma*-tocopherol)**

Origin   Synthetic.

Function   Antioxidant; vitamin.

Adverse   None known in food use.
Effects

Typical   —
Products

E309   **Synthetic *delta*-tocopherol
(Vitamin E; DL-*delta*-tocopherol)**

Origin   Synthetic.

Function   Antioxidant; vitamin.

Adverse   None known in food use.
Effects

Typical   —
Products

E310 **Propyl gallate (Propyl 3,4,5, trihyroxybenzoate)**

Origin Prepared synthetically.

Function Antioxidant in oils and fats.

Adverse Effects All alkyl gallates may cause gastric irritation and problems for people who suffer from asthma or are sensitive to aspirin. One report implies that this substance could cause reproductive failures and liver damage. Not permitted in foods intended for babies or young children. See also pages 12-14.

Typical Products Vegetable oils and
shortenings
Dry breakfast cereals
Margarine
Instant potatoes
Snack foods
Chewing gum

E311   **Octyl gallate**

Origin   Prepared synthetically.

Function   Antioxidant.

Adverse   All alkyl gallates may cause gastric irritation and
Effects   problems for people who suffer from asthma or
                  are sensitive to aspirin. Not permitted in foods
                  intended for babies or young children. See also
                  pages 12-14.

Typical   —
Products

E312   **Dodecyl gallate (Dodecyl 3,4,5, -
                  trihydroxybenzoate)**

Origin   Synthetically prepared.

Function   Antioxidant.

Adverse   All alkyl gallates may cause gastric irritation and
Effects   problems for people who suffer from asthma or
                  are sensitive to aspirin. Not permitted in foods
                  intended for babies or young children. See also
                  pages 12-14.

Typical   —
Products

E320   **Butylated hydroxyanisole (BHA)**

Origin   Prepared synthetically.

Function   Antioxidant for oils and fats either alone or with
                 a gallate and a synergist (see glossary) e.g., citric
                 acid or phosphoric acid. Delays or retards or
                 prevents the development in food of rancidity
                 or other flavour deterioration due to oxidation.
                 It is heat resistant, so effective in baked products.

Adverse   Raises the lipid and cholesterol levels in the blood.
Effects   Can induce the formation of metabolizing
                 enzymes in the liver with an increased risk of
                 breakdown of important substances in the body
                 such as vitamin D. Not permitted in foods
                 intended for babies or young children except to
                 preserve added vitamin A. See also pages 12-14.
                     American work on animals suggests that E320
                 and E321 could possibly protect against some
                 carcinogens.

Typical   Biscuits
Products   Sweets
                 Raisins
                 Fruit pies
                 Soft drinks
                 Margarine
                 Cheese spread
                 Sachet marinade
                 Beef stock cubes
                 Savoury rice
                 Packet convenience
                     foods

E321   Butylated hydroxytoluene (BHT)

Origin   Prepared synthetically.

Function   Antioxidant for food oils and fats.

Adverse
Effects

Some people are sensitive to the presence of BHT in foods, developing rashes. It can cause the development of metabolizing enzymes in the liver which can increase the rate of breakdown of other substances in the body, e.g. vitamin D. Various reports have linked this additive with possible reproductive failures, behavioural effects and blood cell changes. Not permitted in foods intended for babies or young children except to preserve added vitamin A. See also pages 12-14.

American research suggests that BHT increases the life-span of experimental mice. A Danish report, however, claims BHT increases tumour formation in rats. As some manufacturers use, and others do not use, BHT for similar products, the commercial necessity for BHT has been questioned.

Typical
Products

Sachet marinade
Packet cake mix
Savoury rice
Soft and other margarines, shortenings and vegetable oils
Crisps
Salted peanuts
Potato rings
Gravy granules
Dehydrated mashed potato
Dry breakfast cereals
Chewing gum
Packet convenience foods

Emulsifiers, Stabilizers
and Others

E322   **Lecithins**

Origin   Most commercial lecithin is obtained from soya
                  beans. Other commercial sources are egg yolk,
                  leguminous seeds including peanuts and maize,
                  although lecithin is present in all living cells.

Function   Surfactant (surface-active agent); emulsifier;
                  stabilizer; antioxidant and viscosity reducer in
                  chocolate; plasticizer (additional thickness for
                  fats).

Adverse   No known toxicological problems. Used
Effects   experimentally to treat senile dementia and to
                  mobilize fats in the body.

Typical   Chocolate
Products   Powdered milks
                  Soft margarine
                  Confectionery
                  Dessert mixtures
                  Packet trifle mix
                  Vermicelli
                  Chocolate cake
                      covering
                  Yogurt whip
                  Chocolate biscuits
                  Lecithin granules

E325 **Sodium lactate**

Origin The sodium salt of lactic acid.

Function Humectant and substitute for glycerol; synergistic effect on other substances by increasing antioxidant effect.

Adverse Effects Could have a certain toxicity for very young children. No toxicological problems known with adults.

Typical Products Confectionery
Cheese

E326 **Potassium lactate**

Origin The potassium salt of lactic acid.

Function Capable of increasing the antioxidant effect of other substances; buffer.

Adverse Effects None known.

Typical Products —

E327   Calcium lactate

Origin   The calcium salt of lactic acid.

Function   Antioxidant; capable of increasing antioxidant effect of other substances; buffer; firming agent.

Adverse Effects   Not known.

Typical Products   Packet lemon meringue
                    pie mix

E330   Citric acid

Origin
Occurs naturally in lemon and other citrus juices; prepared commercially by the fermentation of molasses with strains of *Aspergillus niger*.

Function
As a synergist to enhance the effectiveness of antioxidants: prevents discolouration of fruit, development of 'off' flavours and retains vitamin C. Stabilizes the acidity of food substances; sequestrant; flavouring; helps jam to set.

Adverse Effects
Citric acid taken in very large quantities may occasionally cause erosion of the teeth and have a local irritant action.

Typical Products
Biscuits
Tinned vegetables
Tinned fruit
Non-alcoholic drinks
Frozen croquette
   potatoes
Frozen potato waffles
Tinned sauces
Treatment of raisins
Ice cream
Packet cake mix
Packet soup mix
Sorbet mix
Wine and cider
Flavouring in drinks
   and confectionery
Jams and jelly preserves
Frozen fish, especially
   herrings, shrimps
   and crab
Bakery products
Cheese

Pasteurized processed
  cheese
Cheese spread
Cream cottage cheese

E331   **Sodium citrates**
E331(a)   **Sodium dihydrogen citrate**
            (*mono*Sodium citrate)

Origin   A sodium salt of citric acid.

Function   Synergistic effect on other antioxidants; buffer;
emulsifying salt; sequestrant; added to infant milk
feeds and invalid food to prevent formation of
large curds.

Adverse   None known.
Effects

Typical   Ice cream
Products   Sweets
             Packet Black Forest
                 gateau mix

E331(b) *di*Sodium citrate

Origin A sodium salt of citric acid.

Function Antioxidant; synergistic effect on other antioxidants; buffer; emulsifying salt.

Adverse Effects None known.

Typical Products
Wines
Fizzy drinks
Processed cheese slices

E331(c) *tri*Sodium citrate (Citrosodine)

Origin A sodium salt of citric acid.

Function Antioxidant; buffer; emulsifying salt; sequestrant.

Adverse Effects None known.

Typical Products Processed cheese

E332   **Potassium dihydrogen citrate**
            (*mono* Potassium citrate)

Origin   A potassium salt of citric acid.

Function   Buffer; emulsifying salt.

Adverse   None known; potassium is rapidly excreted in the
Effects   urine in healthy individuals.

Typical   Sterilized and UHT
Products   cream
              Condensed milk
              Dried milk
              Cheese
              Reduced-sugar jam

E332   ***tri*Potassium citrate**
            (Potassium citrate)

Origin   A potassium salt of citric acid.

Function   Antioxidant; buffer; emulsifying salt; sequestrant.

Adverse   None in foods; in therapeutic amounts may make
Effects   the skin sensitive and cause mouth ulcers to
              develop.

Typical   Confectionery
Products   Wines
              Fizzy drinks
              Cheeses
              Rum sauce
              Crisps
              Biscuits
              Packet convenience
                 dessert mixes and
                 toppings

E333   *mono*, *di*, and *tri* Calcium citrate

Origin   Calcium salts of citric acid.

Function   Buffers; firming agents; emulsifying salts.

Adverse Effects   None in foods; in therapeutic amounts may induce the formation of mouth ulcers.

Typical Products
Wines
Fizzy drinks
Confectionery
Cheeses

E334   L-(+)-Tartaric acid

Origin   Occurs naturally in grapes; sometimes deposited as crystals in wine. Manufactured as a by-product of the wine industry.

Function   Antioxidant; capable of increasing the anxioxidant effect of other substances (synergist); acid; sequestrant (see glossary); diluent for food colours.

Adverse Effects   No known toxicological risks. Strong solutions of tartaric acid are mildly irritant and if ingested undiluted may cause gastro-enteritis.

Typical Products
Confectionery
Jams
Jellies
Marmalades
Fizzy drinks

E335 *mono*Sodium L-(+)-tartrate and *di*Sodium L-(+)-tartrate

Origin Manufactured from tartaric acid.

Function Antioxidant and capable of increasing the antioxidant effect of other substances (synergist); buffer; emulsifying salt; sequestrant.

Adverse Effects No known toxicological risks.

Typical Products Confectionery
Jams
Jellies
Marmalades
Fizzy drinks

Typical Fruit Pie (Apricot)

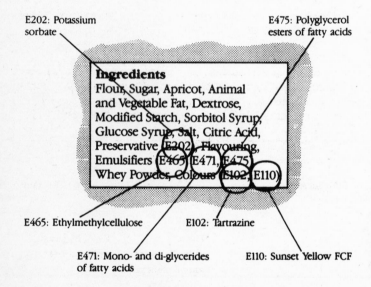

E202: Potassium sorbate

E475: Polyglycerol esters of fatty acids

Ingredients
Flour, Sugar, Apricot, Animal
and Vegetable Fat, Dextrose,
Modified Starch, Sorbitol Syrup,
Glucose Syrup, Salt, Citric Acid,
Preservative (E202), Flavouring,
Emulsifiers (E465) (E471, E475)
Whey Powder, Colours (E102, E110)

E465: Ethylmethylcellulose

E102: Tartrazine

E471: Mono- and di-glycerides of fatty acids

E110: Sunset Yellow FCF

Typical Dessert Mix (Strawberry)

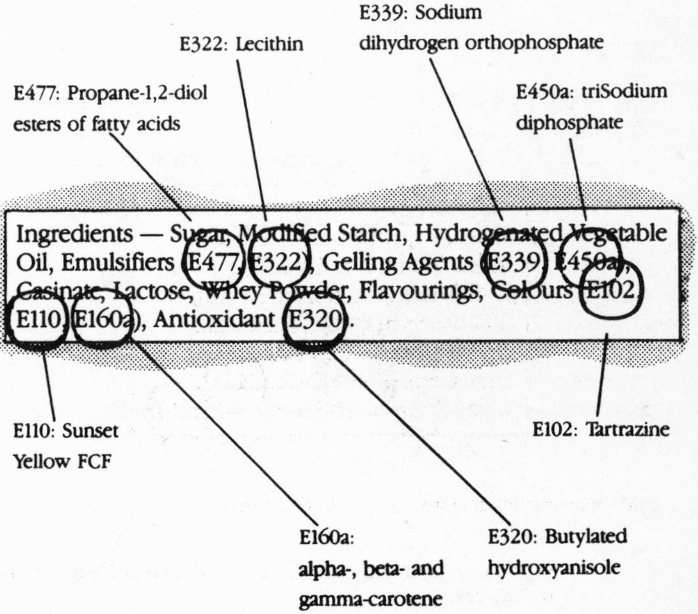

E322: Lecithin

E339: Sodium
dihydrogen orthophosphate

E477: Propane-1,2-diol
esters of fatty acids

E450a: triSodium
diphosphate

Ingredients — Sugar, Modified Starch, Hydrogenated Vegetable Oil, Emulsifiers (E477, E322), Gelling Agents (E339, E450a), Casinate, Lactose, Whey Powder, Flavourings, Colours (E102, E110, E160a), Antioxidant (E320).

E110: Sunset
Yellow FCF

E102: Tartrazine

E160a:
alpha-, beta- and
gamma-carotene

E320: Butylated
hydroxyanisole

E336   *mono* **Potassium L-(+)-tartrate
(Potassium hydrogen tartrate;
Cream of tartar; Potassium
acid tartrate)**

Origin   Prepared from tartaric acid.

Function   Acid; buffer; emulsifying salt; raising agent for
               flour, often used with 500 (Sodium bicarbonate)
               because it works slowly and gives a more
               prolonged evolution of carbon dixoide; inverting
               agent for sugar in boiled sweet manufacture.

Adverse   None known; potassium salts are readily excreted
Effects   by healthy kidneys. The only people at risk are
               those whose kidney or liver functions are
               impaired.

Typical   Packet lemon meringue
Products   pie mix
               Packet lemon meringue
                   crunch mix

E336   *di*Potassium L-(+)-tartrate

Origin   Manufactured from tartaric acid.

Function   Antioxidant and capable of increasing the antioxidant effect of other substances (synergist); buffer; emulsifying salt.

Adverse Effects   No known toxicological risks.

Typical Products
Jelly part of packet
    trifle mix
Packet meringue
    crunch mix

E337   Potassium sodium L-(+)-tartrate (Sodium and potassium tartrate; Sodium potassium tartrate: Rochelle salt)

Origin   The potassium and sodium salts of tartaric acid.

Function   Buffer; emulsifying salt; stabilizer; capable of increasing antioxidant effect of other substances (synergist).

Adverse Effects   No known toxicological problems. The tartrates of the alkali metals are less readily absorbed than the citrates.

Typical Products
Meat and cheese
    products

E338   **Orthophosphoric acid**
               (Phosphoric acid)

Origin   Prepared by the action of sulphuric acid on
               tricalcium phosphate from phosphate rock
               deposits in the United States.

Function   To speed penetration of brine; capable of
               increasing the antioxidant effect of other
               substances (synergist); acid; flavouring and
               sequestrant.

Adverse   None known.
Effects

Typical   Fizzy drinks
Products   Cooked meats and
                  sausages
               Ham
               Cheese

E339(a)   **Sodium dihydrogen orthophosphate**
             N.B. E339, (a), (b), (c) are all classified
             as E339

Origin   Prepared from phosphoric acid.

Function   To improve texture and prevent seepage of serum
             from foods; to speed penetration of brine; anti-
             oxidant synergist; buffer.

Adverse   None known.
Effects

Typical   Cooked meats
Products   Sausages
             Fizzy drinks
             Ham
             Packet cheesecake mix
             Packet lemon pie filling

E339(b)   ***di*Sodium hydrogen orthophosphate**

Origin   Prepared from phosphoric acid.

Function   Buffer; nutrient; gelling agent; stabilizer.

Adverse   None known.
Effects

Typical   Butter/margarine
Products   compound
             Cooked meats
             Ham
             Sausages

109

E339(c)   *tri*Sodium orthophosphate
            (Sodium phosphate tribasic)

Origin   Prepared from phosphoric acid.

Function   Clarifying sugar; emulsifying salt; anti-caking
            agent; buffer; antioxidant synergist.

Adverse   None known.
Effects

Typical   Processed cheese
Products   Cooked meats
            Ham
            Sausages
            Cheese spread
            Processed cheese slices
            Bottled cheese spread
            Instant whipped
               desserts

E340(a)   **Potassium dihydrogen
            orthophosphate (Potassium phosphate
            monobasic)
            N.B. E340 (a), (b), (c) are all classified
            as E340**

Origin   Prepared from phosphoric acid.

Function   Buffer; sequestrant; emulsifying salt; antioxidant
            synergist.

Adverse   None known.
Effects

Typical Products	Jelly part of packet trifle mix Dessert topping

---

E340(b)   **_di_Potassium hydrogen orthophosphate (Potassium phosphate dibasic)**

Origin   Prepared from phosphoric acid.

Function   Buffer; emulsifying salt; antioxidant synergist.

Adverse Effects   None known.

Typical Products   Non-dairy powdered coffee creamers

E340(c)   **_tri_Potassium orthophosphate (Potassium phosphate tribasic)**

Origin   Prepared from phosphoric acid.

Function   Emulsifying salt; antioxidant synergist; buffer.

Adverse Effects   None known.

Typical Products   —

E341(a)   **Calcium tetrahydrogen *di*orthophosphate (acid Calcium phosphate; ACP)**
N.B. E341 (a), (b), (c) are all classified as E341

Origin   Calcium phosphate (apatite) occurs naturally and derivitives of this are produced chemically.

Function   Improving agent; buffer; firming agent; emulsifying salt; sequestrant; yeast food; raising agent in nearly all baking powders; antioxidant synergist.

Adverse Effects   None known.

Typical Products   Short pastry mix
Baking powder

E341(b)   **Calcium hydrogen orthophosphate (Calcium phosphate dibasic)**

Origin   Prepared chemically from naturally derived calcium phosphate.

Function   Emulsifying salt; firming agent; yeast food; nutrient mineral supplement in cereals and other foods; antioxidant synergist; animal feed supplement; abrasive in toothpaste and reduces the incidence of dental caries when added to sweets.

Adverse Effects   None known.

Typical Products   Tinned cherry pie
         filling

E341(c)   *tri*Calcium diorthophosphate

Origin   Prepared chemically from naturally derived calcium phosphate.

Function   Anti-caking agent; buffer; antioxidant synergist; emulsifying salt; nutrient yeast food; diluent for vegetable extracts; abrasive in toothpastes; clarifying sugar syrups.

Adverse Effects   None known.

Typical Products   Cake mixes

350   **Sodium malate**

Origin   A sodium salt of malic acid.

Function   Buffer.

Adverse Effects   None known.

Typical Products   —

Under consideration by the E.E.C. for an 'E' prefix.

350   **Sodium hydrogen malate**

Origin   A sodium salt of malic acid.

Function   Buffer.

Adverse Effects   None known.

Typical Products   —

Under consideration by the E.E.C. for an 'E' prefix.

---

351   **Potassium malate**

Origin   The potassium salt of malic acid.

Function   Buffer.

Adverse Effects   None known.

Typical Products   —

Under consideration by the E.E.C. for an 'E' prefix.

---

352   Calcium malate

Origin   A calcium salt of malic acid.

Function   Buffer; firming agent.

Adverse Effects   None known.

Typical Products   —

Under consideration by the E.E.C. for an 'E' prefix.

352   Calcium hydrogen malate

Origin   A calcium salt of malic acid.

Function   Firming agent.

Adverse Effects   None known.

Typical Products   —

Under consideration by the E.E.C. for an 'E' prefix.

353   Metatartaric acid

Origin   Prepared from tartaric acid.

Function   Sequestrant.

Adverse Effects   None known.

Typical Products

Wine

Under consideration by
  the E.E.C. for an 'E'
  prefix.

---

355   Adipic acid (Hexanedioic acid)

Origin   An organic acid which occurs in many living cells and especially in beet juice. Prepared synthetically for commercial use by oxidizing cyclohexanol with nitric acid..

Function   Acidulating agent; flavouring agent; raising agent in baking powders, since unlike tartaric acid (E334), cream of tartar (E336) and phosphates, adipic acid is not hydroscopic (water attracting).

Adverse Effects   None known.

Typical Products

—

Under consideration by
  the E.E.C. for an 'E'
  prefix.

116

363   Succinic acid

Origin   Occurs naturally in fossils, fungi and lichens but prepared for commercial use from acetic acid.

Function   Acid.

Adverse Effects   None known.

Typical Products   —

Under consideration by the E.E.C. for an 'E' prefix.

370   1,4-Heptonolactone

Origin   Prepared synthetically.

Function   Acid; sequestrant.

Adverse Effects   None known.

Typical Products   —

Under consideration by the E.E.C. for an 'E' prefix.

375	**Nicotinic acid (Niacin; Nicotinamide)**

Origin   Occurs naturally in yeast, liver, rice polishings and lean meats, although it is prepared for commercial use by the oxidation of nicotine with concentrated nitric acid.

Function   B Vitamin; colour protector.

Adverse Effects   Nicotinic acid can dilate the blood vessels and if given in therapeutic doses it may produce flushing of the face, and pounding in the head and a sensation of heat. It is perfectly safe in normal use.

Typical Products   Bread
Flour
Breakfast cereals

Under consideration by
the E.E.C. for an 'E'
prefix.

380	***triAmmonium* citrate**

Origin   Prepared from citric acid.

Function   Buffer; emulsifying salt.

Adverse Effects   None known.

Typical Products   —

Under consideration by
the E.E.C. for an 'E'
prefix.

381 **Ammonium ferric citrate (Ferric ammonium citrate)**

Origin Prepared from citric acid.

Function Dietary iron supplement; used medically for raising the level of red blood cells.

Adverse Effects None known.

Typical Products Iron tablets
Infant milk formulae
Bread flour (not 100% wholemeal)

Under consideration by the E.E.C. for an 'E' prefix.

---

381 **Ammonium ferric citrate, green**

Origin Prepared from citric acid.

Function Dietary iron supplement.

Adverse Effects None known.

Typical Products —

Under consideration by the E.E.C. for an 'E' prefix.

---

385 **Calcium disodium ethylenediamine — NNN'N' tetra-acetate (Calcium disodium EDTA)**

Origin Prepared synthetically.

Function Sequestrant; chelating substance (binds to free metals promoting stabilization of products).

Adverse Effects In larger quantities than would be the case as a food additive calcium disodium EDTA has caused vomiting, diarrhoea and abdominal cramps. There has been some suggestion that the additive may interfere with the body's absorption of essential trace elements, such as iron, zinc and copper.

Typical Products Salad dressings
Alcoholic beverages

Under consideration by
the E.E.C. for an 'E'
prefix.

120

E400   **Alginic acid**

Origin   Extracted from brown seaweeds, mainly *Laminaria*, growing off the west coasts of Scotland and Ireland.

Function   Emulsifier; stabilizer; gelling agent; thickener.

Adverse Effects   Natural product which produces no known toxicological risks.

Typical Products   Ice cream (as stabilizing colloid) ensuring creamy texture and preventing growth of ice crystals
Suspending agent in soft drinks
Puddings
Instant desserts
Custard tarts, etc.

E401 Sodium alginate

Origin Prepared from alginic acid (E400) derived from brown seaweeds.

Function Stabilizing agent; suspending or thickening or emulsifying agent in the preparation of water-mixable pastes, creams and gels. Capable of emulsifying an equal volume of vegetable oil by simple agitation.

Adverse Effects No known toxicological problems.

Typical Products
Desserts
Puddings
Packet cheesecake
    mixes
Ice cream
Packet cake mixes
Processed cheese slices
Barbecue sauce mixes
Tinned fruit pie fillings

E402   **Potassium alginate**

Origin   Prepared from alginic acid (E400) derived from native brown seaweeds.

Function   Emulsifier; stabilizer; boiler water additive; gelling agent.

Adverse Effects   None known.

Typical Products   —

E403   **Ammonium alginate**

Origin   Prepared from alginic acid (E400) derived from native brown seaweeds.

Function   Emulsifier; stabilizer; diluent for colouring matter; thickener.

Adverse Effects   None known.

Typical Products   —

E404   **Calcium alginate (Algin)**

Origin   Prepared from alginic acid (E400) derived from native brown seaweeds.

Function   Emulsifier; stabilizer; thickening agent and gelling agent.

Adverse Effects   None known.

Typical Products   Ice cream
Synthetic cream

E405   **Propane -1, 2 -diol alginate (Propylene gylcol alginate; alginate ester)**

Origin   Prepared from alginic acid derived from native brown seaweeds.

Function   Emulsifier or stabilizer; thickener; solvent for extracts, flavours or spices.

Adverse Effects   None known.

Typical Products   Thousand Island
   dressing
Cottage cheese with
   salmon and
   cucumber
Mint sauce
Seafood dressing
Carton salad

E406 **Agar (agar-agar; Japanese isinglass)**

Origin A naturally occurring derivative of the stems of seaweeds belonging to the red algae family, especially *Gelidium amansii.*

Function Thickening agent; stabilizer and gelling agent.

Adverse Effects Agar is not digested; large quantities of it may temporarily increase flatulence and distension or cause intestinal obstruction but it is likely that amounts in food are too small to produce these effects.

Typical Products Thickening agent for
      ice cream and for
        glazing meats when
          a firm jelly is needed
Frozen raspberry trifle

E407   **Carrageenan (Irish Moss)**

Origin   Natural extract of several seaweeds, notably
                Carragheen *(Chondrus crispus).*

Function   Emulsifying, thickening, suspending and gelling
                agent.

Adverse   Reported to be the possible cause of ulcerative
Effects   colitis and, when degraded, may be carcinogenic.
                The most harmful form is when taken in a drink
                (*Lancet*, 7 Feb. '81, p. 338).

Typical   Ice creams
Products   Desserts
                Jellified fruit juices
                Decorations on cakes
                Pastries
                Biscuits
                Blancmanges
                Chocolate products
                Cheeses
                Quick-setting jelly mix
                Milk shakes
                Spray cream
                Frozen trifle
                Salad dressings
                Sour cream
                Infant formula
                Alcoholic beverages

E410   **Locust bean gum (Ceratonia gum, Carob bean gum)**

Origin   Extract from the seeds of the Locust or Carob tree *Ceratonia silqua)* a member of the pea family, growing in the eastern Mediterranean.

Function   Gelling agent; stabilizer; emulsifier.

Adverse Effects   None known. The sugary pods have been eaten since Biblical times (and are sometimes referred to as St John's bread).

Typical Products
Jelly part of packet
    trifle mix
Italian ice cream
Tinned cherry pie
    filling
Carton salad (celery
    apple and orange)
Salad cream

E412   **Guar gum (Jaguar gum, guar flour, Cluster bean)**

Origin   A gum extracted from the stored food in the seeds of *Cyamopsis tetragonolobus*, or *C. psoraloides* a member of the pea family native to India, the drier tropics and grown in the south western areas of the United States as a cattle feed.

Function   Thickening agent; emulsion stabilizer; suspending agent; dietary bulking agent; helps diabetics control blood sugar levels.

Adverse Effects   These only occur when excessively large quantities are consumed and can include nausea, flatulence and abdominal cramps.

Typical Products
Bottled barbecue sauce
Carton salad
Scotch eggs
Salad dressings
Packet soups
Packet meringue
   crunch mix
Tinned chicken in
   white sauce
Brown sauce
Piccalilli
Horseradish cream
Sauce tartare
Carton coleslaw
Milkshake
Ice cream
Frozen fruit
Icings and glazes
Fruit drinks

| E413 | **Tragacanth (Gum dragon, gum tragacanth)** |

Origin   Tragacanth gum exudes from the trunk and branches of *Astragalus gummifer* and other species of the same genera (pea family). It may flow naturally or be collected by incision in the same way as rubber is from small bushes which grow sparsely in mountain locations in Iran, Iraq, Turkey, Russia and other parts of the Middle East.

Function   Emulsifier; stabilizer; thickener; prevention of crystallization in sugar confectionery.

Adverse Effects   Adverse reactions have only occurred rarely and contact dermatitis has been reported when tragacanth was used on the skin.

Typical Products
Cottage cheese with
   salmon and
   cucumber
Cake decorations
Piccalilli
Salad dressings
Processed cheese
Cream cheese
Sherbet

E414   **Gum arabic (Acacia; Sudan gum; Gum Hashab; Kordofan gum)**

Origin   The dried gum which flows from the stems and branches of *Acacia senegal* and other African Acacia trees (members of the pea family). It collects and dries in walnut-sized globules. The trees grow in barren regions of Africa and the Middle East especially along a 3,000 km band following the southern frontier of the Sahara desert.

Function   To retard sugar crystallization; thickener; emulsifier; stabilizer and glazing agent.

Adverse Effects   A few people have demonstrated hypersensitivity to gum arabic after breathing it in or eating it.

Typical Products   Packet Black Forest
   gateau mix

E415   **Xanthan gum (Corn sugar gum)**

Origin   Produced by the fermentation of a carbohydrate
               with a bacterium called *Xanthomonas campestris*.

Function   Stabilizer; thickener; emulsifier.

Adverse   None known.
Effects

Typical   Seafood dressing
Products   Carton coleslaw and
                   carton salads
               Horseradish cream
               Frozen pizza
               Packet dessert topping
               Tinned cherry pie
                   filling
               Sweet pickle

---

416   **Karaya Gum (Sterculia gum)**

Origin   A gum which is collected from the woody tissue
               of members of the *Sterculiaceae* family, native
               from southern China to Indo-China.

Function   Stabilizer; emulsifier; thickener.

Adverse   None known.
Effects

Typical   Some cheeses
Products   Fruit sauce
               Spicy brown sauce
               Piccalilli

Typical Cake Mix

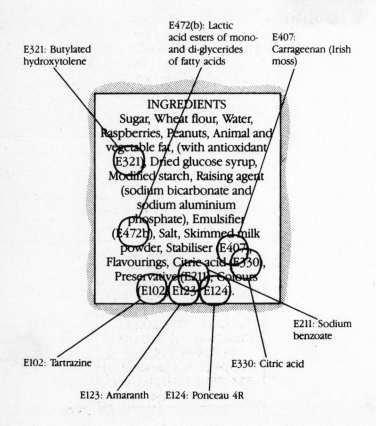

E321: Butylated hydroxytolene

E472(b): Lactic acid esters of mono- and di-glycerides of fatty acids

E407: Carrageenan (Irish moss)

INGREDIENTS
Sugar, Wheat flour, Water, Raspberries, Peanuts, Animal and vegetable fat, (with antioxidant E321), Dried glucose syrup, Modified starch, Raising agent (sodium bicarbonate and sodium aluminium phosphate), Emulsifier (E472b), Salt, Skimmed milk powder, Stabiliser (E407), Flavourings, Citric acid (E330), Preservative (E211), Colours (E102, E123, E124).

E211: Sodium benzoate

E102: Tartrazine

E330: Citric acid

E123: Amaranth   E124: Ponceau 4R

Typical Cake Mix

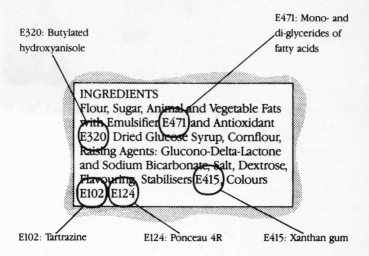

E320: Butylated hydroxyanisole

E471: Mono- and di-glycerides of fatty acids

INGREDIENTS
Flour, Sugar, Animal and Vegetable Fats with Emulsifier E471 and Antioxidant E320 Dried Glucose Syrup, Cornflour, Raising Agents: Glucono-Delta-Lactone and Sodium Bicarbonate, Salt, Dextrose, Flavouring, Stabilisers E415, Colours E102 E124

E102: Tartrazine

E124: Ponceau 4R

E415: Xanthan gum

Typical Yogurt (Honey Muesli Flavour)

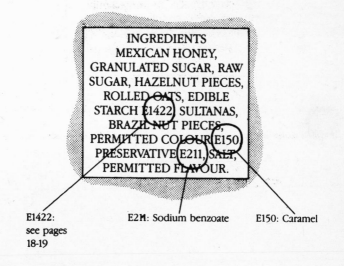

INGREDIENTS
MEXICAN HONEY, GRANULATED SUGAR, RAW SUGAR, HAZELNUT PIECES, ROLLED OATS, EDIBLE STARCH E1422 SULTANAS, BRAZIL NUT PIECES, PERMITTED COLOUR E150 PRESERVATIVE E211, SALT, PERMITTED FLAVOUR.

E1422:
see pages
18-19

E211: Sodium benzoate

E150: Caramel

E420(i)   **Sorbitol**
E420(ii) **Sorbitol syrup**

Origin   A six-carbon sugar alcohol which occurs naturally
              in some fruits and is metabolized in the body but
              is synthesized chemically from glucose for
              commercial use.

Function   Sweetening agent and substitute for glycerol.
              When added to syrups containing sucrose it
              reduces the tendency to deposit crystals on
              storage. Also as a humectant and stabilizer.

Adverse   Excessive amounts could cause flatulence,
Effects   diarrhoea and abdominal distension. Useful for
              diabetics as it does not raise the blood sugar level
              significantly, and is well tolerated.

Typical   Chocolates
Products   Confectionery
              Pastries
              Ice cream
              Food colour diluent
              Diabetic jam
              Prepackaged cakes

E421   Mannitol (Manna sugar)

Origin
Occurs naturally in the wood of coniferous trees. Generally prepared from seaweed or manna, the dried exudate of *Fraxinus ornus* which grows in Mediterranean countries.

Function
Texturizing agent; dietary supplement; humectant; sweetener in sugar-free products; anti-caking agent.

Adverse Effects
Hypersensitivity reactions have occurred occasionally and mannitol may cause nausea, vomiting and diarrhoea.

Typical Products
Sweets
Ice cream

E422   Glycerol

Origin
Occurs naturally in many plant cells, synthesized by the plants themselves. Obtained commercially from oils and fats as a by-product in the manufacture of soaps and fatty acids.

Function
Solvent (see page 18); humectant; sweetener.

Adverse Effects
Very large doses by mouth can produce effects such as headache, thirst, nausea and high blood sugar levels.

Typical Products
Liqueurs
Confectionery
Cake icing

430   **Polyoxyethylene (8) stearate (Polyoxyl 8 stearate)**

Origin   Manufactured from fatty acid molecules.

Function   Emulsifier; stabilizer.

Adverse Effects   Some people who have allergic skin reactions are allergic to macrogol stearate. There has been some suggestion that this additive may have an effect on the gastrointestinal and urinary tracts, forming kidney stones etc.

Typical Products   Bakery foods

Under consideration by the E.E.C. for an 'E' prefix.

431   **Polyoxyethylene stearate (Polyoxyl 40 stearate)**

Origin   Manufactured from fatty acids.

Function   Emulsifier.

Adverse Effects   A small proportion of people with skin allergy show allergic reactions to macrogol stearate.

Typical Products   —

Under consideration by the E.E.C. for an 'E' prefix.

432   **Polyoxyethylene (20) sorbitan monolaurate (Polysorbate 20; Tween 20)**

Origin   Prepared from sorbitol.

Function   Emulsifier; stabilizer.

Adverse Effects   None known.

Typical Products   —

Under consideration by
   the E.E.C. for an 'E'
   prefix.

433   **Polyoxyethylene (20) sorbitan mono-oleate (Polysorbate 80; Tween 80)**

Origin   Prepared from sorbitol.

Function   Emulsifier; stabilizer.

Adverse Effects   None known.

Typical Products   —

Under consideration by
   the E.E.C. for an 'E'
   prefix.

434   **Polyoxyethylene (20) sorbitan monopalmitate (Polysorbate 40; Tween 40)**

Origin   Prepared from sorbitol.

Function   Emulsifier; stabilizer.

Adverse Effects   Polysorbates may increase the absorption of liquid paraffin and other fat-soluble substances.

Typical Products   —

Under consideration by the E.E.C. for an 'E' prefix.

435   **Polyoxyethylene (20) sorbitan monostearate (Polysorbate 60; Tween 60)**

Origin   Prepared from sorbitol.

Function   Emulsifier; stabilizer.

Adverse Effects   Polysorbates may increase the absorption of liquid paraffin and other fat-soluble substances.

Typical Products   Packet cake mix

Under consideration by the E.E.C. for an 'E' prefix.

436 Polyoxyethylene (20) sorbitan tristearate (Polysorbate 65; Tween 65)

Origin   Prepared from sorbitol.

Function   Emulsifier; stabilizer.

Adverse   Polysorbates may increase the absorption of
Effects   liquid paraffin and other fat-soluble substances.

Typical   —
Products

                  Under consideration by
                     the E.E.C. for an 'E'
                     prefix.

E440(a)   Pectin

Origin   Protopectin is present between the cell walls of plants, cementing them together. During the ripening process of acid fruits (especially apples, plums, bitter oranges and lemons) protopectin accumulates and as the fruit matures, enzymes break down the protopectin to the softer pectin. Apple residues from cider-making and orange pith are the commercial sources of pectin.

Function   Efficient emulsifying and gelling agent in acid media.

Adverse Effects   No real toxicological risks. Large amounts may cause temporary flatulence or intestinal distension.

Typical Products   Jams
Jellies
Marmalades
Flans
Puddings
Desserts

E440(a)   Ammonium pectate

Origin   Prepared from pectin.

Function   Stabilizer; gelling agent; thickener.

Adverse Effects   None known.

Typical Products   Jams
Jellies

E440(a)   **Potassium pectate**

Origin   Prepared from pectin.

Function   Emulsifying, stabilizing or gelling agent.

Adverse Effects   None known.

Typical Products   Jams
Preserves

E440(a)   **Sodium pectate**

Origin   Prepared from pectin.

Function   Gelling agent; emulsifier; stabilizer.

Adverse Effects   None known.

Typical Products   Jams
Preserves

E440(b)	**Amidated pectin**
Origin	Treatment of pectin extracted from citrus fruits or apples with ammonia, under alkaline conditions.
Function	Emulsifier; stabilizer; gelling agent; thickener.
Adverse Effects	None known.
Typical Products	Jams Preserves

442	**Ammonium phosphatides (Emulsifier YN)**
Origin	Prepared synthetically.
Function	Stabilizer; emulsifier.
Adverse Effects	None known.
Typical Products	Cocoa and chocolate products Under consideration by the E.E.C. for an 'E' prefix.

E450(a)   *di*Sodium dihydrogen diphosphate
               (*di*Sodium dihydrogen pyrophosphate;
               acid sodium pyrophosphate)

Origin   A sodium salt of phosphoric acid.

Function   Buffer; sequestrant; emulsifier; raising agent for
               flour; colour improver; chelating agent (see
               glossary p. 219).

Adverse   None known.
Effects

Typical   Bread
Products   Catering whipping
                   cream
                Cheese
                Condensed milk and
                   dried milk products

E450(a)   **triSodium diphosphate**

Origin   A sodium salt of phosphoric acid.

Function   Buffer; sequestrant; emulsifier; raising agent for
               flour; colour improver; chelating agent (see
               glossary p. 219).

Adverse   None known.
Effects

Typical   Bread
Products   Whipping cream
                   (catering)
                Cheese
                Condensed milk
                Dried milk products

143

E450(a)   *tetra*Sodium diphosphate (*tetra*Sodium pyrosphate)

Origin   Prepared synthetically.

Function   Buffer; emulsifying salt; sequestrant; gelling agent; stabilizer.

Adverse Effects   None known.

Typical Products
Cheese
Catering whipping
    cream
Condensed milk
Dried milk products
Frozen turkey meat loaf

E450(a)   *tetra*Potassium diphosphate

Origin   Prepared synthetically.

Function   Emulsifying salt.

Adverse Effects   None known.

Typical Products
Instant whipped
    desserts
Packet cheesecake mix
Packet cake mix
Cheese spread
Ham and cooked meats

E450(b)   *penta*Sodium triphosphate
              (Sodium tripolyphosphate)

Origin   Prepared synthetically.

Function   Emulsifying salt; texturizer.

Adverse   There is a French suggestion that polyphosphates
Effects   could cause digestive disturbances by the
              blockage of a number of enzymes.

Typical   Cheeses
Products   Unsweetened
              condensed milk

E450(b)   *penta*Potassium triphosphate
              (Potassium tripolyphosphate)

Origin   Prepared synthetically.

Function   Emulsifying salt; texturizer.

Adverse   There is a French suggestion that polyphosphates
Effects   could cause digestive disturbances by the
              blockage of a number of enzymes.

Typical   Tinned hot dog
Products   sausages

145

E450(c)   **Sodium polyphosphates**

Origin   Prepared synthetically.

Function   Emulsifying salts; sequestrants; stabilizers.

Adverse   There is a French suggestion that polyphosphates
Effects   could cause digestive disturbances by the
                blockage of a number of enzymes.

Typical   Tinned custard
Products   Reduced sugar jam
                    products
                Cheeses
                Frozen turkey meat loaf
                Frozen fish fingers and
                    fishcakes

E450(c)   **Potassium polyphosphates**

Origin   Prepared synthetically.

Function   Emulsifying salts; stabilizers.

Adverse   There is a French suggestion that polyphosphates
Effects   could cause digestive disturbances by the
                blockage of a number of enzymes.

Typical   Cheeses
Products   Unsweetened
                    condensed milk
                    products

146

E460   **Microcrystalline cellulose**

Origin   The cellulose walls of plant fibres which are chemically fragmented into microscopic crystals.

Function   Non-nutritive bulking agent; binder; anti-caking agent; dietary fibre; hydration aid; emulsion stabilizer; heat stabilizer; alternative ingredient; tabletting binder and disintegrant; carrier and microdispersant for quick drying; cellulose component and for texture modification.

Adverse Effects   None known.

Typical Products
High-fibre bread
Low-calorie cake,
    biscuits and sweets
Reduced calorie bread
Imitation Mozzarella
    cheese
Grated and shredded
    cheese
Colours, flavours and
    food acids
Expanded snacks
Simulated fruit pieces
Imitation spices
Dehydrated foods

E460	**Alpha-cellulose (Powdered cellulose)**
Origin	The cellulose component of plant cell walls which is disintegrated mechanically to form a pulp which is then dried.
Function	Bulking aid; anti-caking agent; binder; dispersant; thickening agent and filter aid.
Adverse Effects	None known.
Typical Products	— Not permitted in food intended specifically for babies or young children.

E461	**Methylcellulose (Methocel; cologel)**
Origin	Prepared from wood pulp by treatment with alkali and methyl chloride.
Function	Emulsifier; stabilizer; thickener; bulking and binding agent; film former and as a substitute for water soluble gums.
Adverse Effects	None known.
Typical Products	Frozen bubble and squeak Potato waffles

E463 Hydroxypropylcellulose

Origin   Synthetically prepared ether of cellulose.

Function   Stabilizer in foams and lotions; emulsifier; thickener; suspending agent.

*Adverse
Effects*   None known.

*Typical
Products*   —

E464 Hydroxypropylmethylcellulose (Hypromellose)

Origin   Prepared from cellulose.

Function   Gelling or suspending agent; emulsifier; stabilizer and thickening agent.

*Adverse
Effects*   None known.

*Typical
Products*   Frozen waffles

E465 Ethylmethylcellulose (Methylethylcellulose)

Origin Prepared from cellulose.

Function Emulsifier; stabilizer; foaming agent.

Adverse Effects None known.

Typical Products —

E466　　　**Carboxymethylcellulose, sodium salt (Carmellose sodium; CMC)**

Origin　　　Prepared by treating alkali cellulose chemically.

Function　　Thickening agent; texture modification; stabilizer; moisture migration control; gelling agent; non-nutritive bulking agent; opacifier etc.

Adverse Effects　　One report suggests that this substance may cause intestinal obstruction, but generally safe.

Typical Products

Packet cheesecake and
　　cake mixes
Icings
Bakery fillings
Fruit bar filling
Lemon pie filling
Meringues
Dips and spreads
Tinned potato salad
Tinned cream soups
Frozen whipped
　　toppings
Whipped topping basis
Sterilized whipping
　　cream
Ice cream
Milk shake
Frozen mousses
Tomato sauces
Salad dressings
Frozen chips
Frozen fish sticks
Batter coatings
Low-calorie orange
　　squash
Processed cheese
Cottage cheese

E470 **Sodium, potassium and calcium salts of fatty acids (Soaps)**

Origin Prepared chemically.

Function Emulsifiers; stabilizers; anti-caking agents.

Adverse None known.
Effects

Typical Packet Black Forest
Products   gateau mix
Crispy snacks
Shaped crisps

E471	**Mono- and di-glycerides of fatty acids (Glyceryl monostearate, distearate)**
Origin	A normal product of digestion, but prepared for commercial use from glycerin and fatty acids.
Function	Emulsifiers; stabilizers; thickening agents.
Adverse Effects	None known.

Typical Products	Packet Black Forest gateau mixes
	Low-cholesterol margarine
	Quick custard mix
	Hot chocolate mix
	Dried potato flakes
	Dehydrated mashed potato
	Packet dessert topping
	Prepacked cakes
	Jam sponge pudding (pre-packed)
	Shaped crisps
	Aerosol cream
	Packet savoury meal mix
	Mousse mix

E472(a)   **Acetic acid esters of mono- and di-glycerides of fatty acids (Acetylated mono- and di-glycerides; acetoglycerides; complete and partial glycerol esters)**

Origin   Prepared from acetic acid.

Function   Emulsifiers; stabilizers; coating agents; texture modifying agents; solvents and lubricants.

Adverse Effects   None known.

Typical Products   Packet cheesecake mix
Packet dessert topping
Packet mousse mix

E472(b)   **Lactic acid esters of mono- and di-glycerides of fatty acids (Lactylated mono- and di-glycerides; Lactoglycerides)**

Origin   Prepared from lactic acid.

Function   Emulsifiers; stabilizers.

Adverse Effects   None known.

Typical Products   Packet cheesecake mixes
Packet dessert topping
Packet mousse mix

E472(c) **Citric acid esters of mono- and di-glycerides of fatty acids (Citroglycerides)**

Origin Prepared from citric acid.

Function Emulsifiers and stabilizers.

Adverse Effects None known.

Typical Products Packet dessert topping

E472(d) **Tartaric acid esters of mono- and di-glycerides of fatty acids**

Origin Prepared from tartaric acid.

Function Emulsifiers and stabilizers.

Adverse Effects None known.

Typical Products —

E472(e)   **Mono- and diacetyltartaric acid esters of mono- and di-glycerides of fatty acids**

Origin   Prepared from tartaric acid.

Function   Emulsifiers; stabilizers.

Adverse Effects   None known.

Typical Products   Hot chocolate mix
                      Brown bread rolls
                      Frozen pizza
                      Gravy granules

E473   **Sucrose esters of fatty acids**

Origin   Prepared from fatty acids.

Function   Emulsifiers; stabilizers.

Adverse Effects   None known.

Typical Products   —

E474   **Sucroglycerides**

Origin   Prepared by the action of sucrose on natural triglycerides (from lard, tallow, palm oil etc.).

Function   Emulsifiers; stabilizers.

Adverse   None known.
Effects

Typical   —
Products

E475   **Polyglycerol esters of fatty acids**

Origin   Prepared synthetically.

Function   Emulsifiers; stabilizers.

Adverse   None known.
Effects

Typical   Packet cheesecake and
Products   cake mixes
                  Prepacked sponge
                     pudding
                  Prepacked cakes

| 476 | **Polyglycerol esters of polycondensed fatty acids of castor oil (Polyglycerol polyricinoleate)** |

Origin   Prepared from castor oil.

Function   Emulsifier; stabilizer.

Adverse Effects   None known.

Typical Products   —

Under consideration by
the EEC for an 'E'
prefix.

| E477 | **Propane -1,2 - diol esters of fatty acids (Propylene glycol esters of fatty acids)** |

Origin   Prepared from propylene glycol.

Function   Emulsifier; stabilizer.

Adverse Effects   None known.

Typical Products   Packet cake mix
Instant dessert

---

478   **Lactylated fatty acid esters of glycerol and propane -1,2-diol**

Origin   Prepared from lactic acid.

Function   Emulsifiers, stabilizers, whipping agents, plasticizers, surface-active agents.

Adverse Effects   None known.

Typical Products   —

Under consideration by
    the E.E.C. for an 'E'
    prefix.

E481   **Sodium stearoyl-2-lactylate**

Origin   Prepared from lactic acid.

Function   Stabilizer; emulsifier.

Adverse Effects   None known.

Typical Products   Biscuits
Bread
Cakes

Typical Soft Margarine

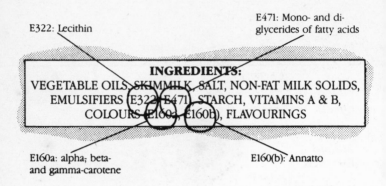

E322: Lecithin

E471: Mono- and di-glycerides of fatty acids

INGREDIENTS:
VEGETABLE OILS, SKIMMILK, SALT, NON-FAT MILK SOLIDS, EMULSIFIERS (E322, E471), STARCH, VITAMINS A & B, COLOURS (E160a, E160b), FLAVOURINGS

E160a: alpha, beta- and gamma-carotene

E160(b): Annatto

Typical Cheese Spread

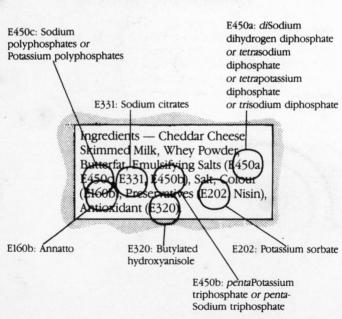

E450c: Sodium polyphosphates *or* Potassium polyphosphates

E450a: *di*Sodium dihydrogen diphosphate *or tetra*sodium diphosphate *or tetra*potassium diphosphate *or* trisodium diphosphate

E331: Sodium citrates

Ingredients — Cheddar Cheese, Skimmed Milk, Whey Powder, Butterfat, Emulsifying Salts (E450a, E450c, E331, E450b), Salt, Colour (E160b), Preservatives (E202, Nisin), Antioxidant (E320)

E160b: Annatto

E320: Butylated hydroxyanisole

E202: Potassium sorbate

E450b: *penta*Potassium triphosphate *or penta*-Sodium triphosphate

Typical Marmalade (Lime Flavour)

E440(a): Pectin *or* Potassium pectate *or* Sodium pectate

E142: Green S (Acid Brilliant Green BS; Lissamine Green)

E331: Sodium citrates

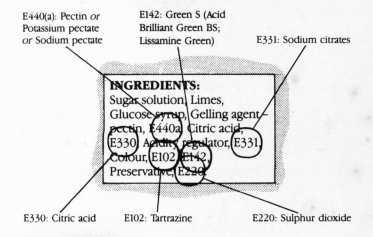

INGREDIENTS:
Sugar solution, Limes, Glucose syrup, Gelling agent—pectin, E440a, Citric acid, E330, Acidity regulator, E331, Colour, E102, E142, Preservative, E220.

E330: Citric acid

E102: Tartrazine

E220: Sulphur dioxide

E482   **Calcium stearoyl-2-lactylate**

Origin   Prepared synthetically.

Function   Emulsifier; stabilizer; whipping aid.

Adverse   None known.
Effects

Typical   Gravy granules
Products

E483   **Stearyl tartrate**

Origin   Prepared from tartaric acid.

Function   Stabilizer; emulsifier.

Adverse   None known.
Effects

Typical   —
Products

491   Sorbitan monostearate

Origin   Prepared synthetically from stearic acid.

Function   Emulsifier; stabilizer; glazing agent.

Adverse
Effects   None known.

Typical   Packet cake mix
Products

     Under consideration by
       the E.E.C. for an 'E'
       prefix.

492   Sorbitan tristearate (Span 65)

Origin   Prepared synthetically from stearic acid.

Function   Emulsifier; stabilizer.

Adverse
Effects   Polysorbates may increase the body's absorption
     of liquid paraffin and fat-soluble substances.

Typical   —
Products

     Under consideration by
       the E.E.C. for an 'E'
       prefix.

493   **Sorbitan monolaurate (Span 20)**

Origin   Prepared from lauric acid.

Function   Emulsifier, stabilizer, antifoaming agent.

Adverse Effects   None known.

Typical Products   —

Under consideration by
the E.E.C. for an 'E'
prefix.

---

494   **Sorbitan mono-oleate (Span 80)**

Origin   Prepared synthetically from oleic acid.

Function   Stabilizer; emulsifier.

Adverse Effects   None known.

Typical Products   —

Under consideration by
the E.E.C. for an 'E'
prefix.

---

495   Sorbitan monopalmitate (Span 40)

Origin   Prepared synthetically.

Function   Oil-soluble emulsifier; stabilizer.

Adverse Effects   None known.

Typical Products   —

Under consideration by
the E.E.C. for an 'E'
prefix.

500   Sodium carbonate

Origin   Although naturally occurring as saline residues deposited from the water of alkaline lakes, it is cheaper to manufacture by the Solvay process or electrolytically from sea or saline lake waters.

Function   Base.

Adverse Effects   None known in small doses. Large amounts can corrode the gut, cause gastric upsets and circulation problems.

Typical Products   Tinned custard

Under consideration by
the E.E.C. for an 'E'
prefix.

500   **Sodium hydrogen carbonate (Sodium bicarbonate; baking soda; Bicarbonate of soda)**

Origin   Prepared synthetically.

Function   Base; aerating agent; diluent.

Adverse Effects   None known.

Typical Products   Tinned custard

Under consideration by
   the EEC for an 'E'
   prefix.

---

500   **Sodium sesquicarbonate (Trona)**

Origin   Occurs naturally in saline residues with other minerals formed in the same way, in California, Mexico and Egypt. Prepared synthetically.

Function   Base.

Adverse Effects   None known.

Typical Products   —

Under consideration by
   the E.E.C. for an 'E'
   prefix.

---

501 Potassium carbonate and Potassium hydrogen carbonate

Origin   Prepared synthetically.

Function   Base; alkali.

Adverse Effects   None known.

Typical Products   —

Under consideration by the E.E.C. for an 'E' prefix.

---

503 Ammonium carbonate (Hartshorn)

Origin   Prepared synthetically.

Function   Buffer; neutralizing agent.

Adverse Effects   None known.

Typical Products   Baking powder

Under consideration by the E.E.C. for an 'E' prefix.

---

503   Ammonium hydrogen carbonate (Ammonium bicarbonate)

Origin   Prepared by passing an excess of carbon dioxide through concentrated ammonia water.

Function   Alkali; buffer; aerating agent.

Adverse Effects   Irritates the mucous membranes of the stomach.

Typical Products   —

Under consideration by
    the E.E.C. for an 'E'
    prefix.

504   Magnesium carbonate (Magnesite)

Origin   Magnesite occurs naturally in serpentine deposits in Greece and India and replacing dolomite and limestone in Austria, Manchuria, Washington and Quebec.

Function   Alkali; anti-caking agent; acidity regulator.

Adverse Effects   None known.

Typical Products   Table salt
Icing sugar
Soured cream
Butter
Ice cream

Under consideration by
    the E.E.C. for an 'E'
    prefix.

507 Hydrochloric acid

Origin Prepared synthetically; one of the chemicals produced in the stomach to assist the digestive process.

Function Acid.

Adverse Effects None known.

Typical Products —

Under consideration by
  the E.E.C. for an 'E'
  prefix.

508 Potassium chloride

Origin Occurs naturally as a saline residue associated with rock salt, and around volcanic vents.

Function Gelling agent; salt substitute; dietary supplement.

Adverse Effects Can, in large doses, cause intestinal ulceration, sometimes with haemorrhage and perforation. Gastric ulceration may occur with sustained release tablets. Unpleasant taste in solution can cause nausea and vomiting.

Typical Products Salt substitute

Under consideration by
  the E.E.C. for an 'E'
  prefix.

509   **Calcium chloride**

Origin   Obtained as a by-product of the solvay process and is also a product from natural salt brines.

Function   Sequestrant; firming agent.

Adverse Effects   None known.

Typical Products

Tinned red kidney
    beans
Pickled red cabbage

Under consideration by
    the E.E.C. for an 'E'
    prefix.

---

510   **Ammonium chloride**

Origin   Prepared synthetically.

Function   Yeast food; flavour.

Adverse Effects   Ammonium chloride is readily absorbed by the food canal and may decrease the acidity of the urine. It should be avoided by people with imperfect liver or kidney functions.

Typical Products

—

Under consideration by
    the E.E.C. for an 'E'
    prefix.

---

513   **Sulphuric acid**

Origin   Prepared synthetically.

Function   Acid.

Adverse Effects   Poisonous.

Typical Products   —

Under consideration by
the E.E.C. for an 'E'
prefix.

514   **Sodium sulphate**

Origin   Occurs naturally as thenardite and mirabilite, and the U.S.S.R. Canada and the U.S.A. are the chief producers.

Function   Diluent.

Adverse Effects   Although the healthy body can adapt to a wide range of sodium intake daily, excessive sodium can be dangerous because it is closely related to the body's water balance. Those at greatest risk are small babies and people suffering with kidney and heart complaints.

Typical Products   —

Under consideration by
the E.E.C. for an 'E'
prefix.

515   Potassium sulphate

Origin

Occurs in nature as a triple sulphate of potassium magnesium and calcium particularly at Stassfurt in Germany.

Function

Salt substitute for dietetic use.

Adverse Effects

None known.

Typical Products

—

Under consideration by the E.E.C. for an 'E' prefix.

---

516   Calcium sulphate (Gypsum, Plaster of Paris)

Origin

A naturally occurring mineral; commercial sources are the U.S.A. and France, followed by Spain, Great Britain and Canada.

Function

Firming agent; sequestrant; nutrient; yeast food; inert excipient.

Adverse Effects

None known.

Typical Products

—

Under consideration by the E.E.C. for an 'E' prefix.

---

518   **Magnesium sulphate — (Epsom salts, Espomite)**

Origin   Occurs in solution in sea- and mineral-waters and is deposited from the waters of saline lakes and as crusts in limestone caves.

Function   Dietary supplement; firming agent; used in making 'Burton' style beer.

Adverse Effects   Magnesium is not absorbed to any large extent by the body so that toxicity is not a problem except to people whose kidneys are functioning imperfectly.

Typical Products   —

Under consideration by
the E.E.C. for an 'E'
prefix.

524   **Sodium hydroxide**

Origin   Prepared synthetically.

Function   Base; colour solvent.

Adverse Effects   None known.

Typical Products   Jams and preserves

Under consideration by
the E.E.C. for an 'E'
prefix.

173

525   Potassium hydroxide

Origin   Manufactured synthetically.

Function   Base.

Adverse Effects   Unless it is very dilute, the caustic nature of this chemical causes immediate burning pain in the mouth, throat and stomach and the lining membranes become swollen and detached. Vomiting, pain and shock result.

Typical Products   Cocoa products

Under consideration by
    the E.E.C. for an 'E'
    prefix.

526   Calcium hydroxide

Origin   Prepared by the hydration of lime.

Function   Firming agent, neutralizing agent.

Adverse Effects   None known.

Typical Products   Cheese
Cocoa products
Shaped crisps

Under consideration by
    the E.E.C. for an 'E'
    prefix.

527   Ammonium hydroxide

Origin   Prepared synthetically.

Function   Food colouring diluent and solvent; alkali.

Adverse   None known.
Effects

Typical   Food colours
Products   Cocoa products

              Under consideration by
                the E.E.C. for an 'E'
                prefix.

---

528   Magnesium hydroxide

Origin   Occurs in nature as the mineral periclase. It is prepared commercially from magnesite ores.

Function   Alkali.

Adverse   None known.
Effects

Typical   Cocoa products
Products

              Under consideration by
                the E.E.C. for an 'E'
                prefix.

---

529   **Calcium oxide**

Origin   Prepared from limestone.

Function   Alkali; nutrient.

*Adverse   None known.
Effects*

---

*Typical   Some cocoa products.
Products*
                  Under consideration by
                     the E.E.C. for an 'E'
                     prefix.

---

530   **Magnesium oxide
                  (Periclase; Native magnesium)**

Origin   A naturally occurring mineral particularly in rocks
                  which have undergone change brought about by
                  pressure and heat.

Function   Anti-caking agent; alkali.

*Adverse   None known.
Effects*

---

*Typical   Some cocoa products
Products*
                  Under consideration by
                     the E.E.C. for an 'E'
                     prefix.

---

535   Sodium ferrocyanide (Sodium hexacyanoferrate II)

Origin   Manufactured synthetically.

Function   Anti-caking agent; crystal modifier.

Adverse Effects   There is a very strong chemical bondage between the iron and cyanide groups which prevents ferrocyanides from having a high order of toxicity.

Typical Products   —

Under consideration by
the E.E.C. for an 'E'
prefix.

536   Potassium ferrocyanide (Potassium hexacyanoferrate II)

Origin   Prepared synthetically.

Function   Anti-caking agent.

Adverse Effects   Because the iron and cyanide groups are strongly bonded there is a very low level of toxicity.

Typical Products   Some wines

Under consideration by
the E.E.C. for an 'E'
prefix.

540   *di*Calcium diphosphate (Calcium hydrogen phosphate; Calcium phosphate dibasic)

Origin   Occurs in nature as the mineral monetite, also prepared synthetically.

Function   Mineral supplement in cereals and other foods. Buffer; neutralizing agent; dietary supplement; raising agent.

Adverse Effects   Little *di*calcium diphosphate is absorbed by the intestines and there is little danger of any adverse reaction.

Typical Products   Some cheeses
Shaped crisps

Under consideration by the E.E.C. for an 'E' prefix.

---

541   **Sodium aluminium phosphate, acidic**

Origin   Prepared synthetically.

Function   Acid; raising agent for flour.

Adverse Effects   Although the healthy body can adapt to a wide range of sodium intake daily, excessive sodium can be dangerous because it is closely related to the body's water balance. Those at greatest risk are small babies and people suffering with kidney and heart complaints.

Typical Products	Packet cake mixes
	Under consideration by the E.E.C. for an 'E' prefix.

541   Sodium aluminium phosphate, basic

Origin	Prepared synthetically.
Function	Emulsifying salt.
Adverse Effects	None known.

Typical Products	—
	Under consideration by the E.E.C. for an 'E' prefix.

542   Edible bone phosphate

Origin	The degreased steam-extract from animal bones.
Function	Anti-caking agent; mineral supplement; filler in tablet making.
Adverse Effects	None known.

Typical Products	—
	Under consideration by the E.E.C. for an 'E' prefix.

544   Calcium polyphosphates

Origin   Prepared synthetically.

Function   Emulsifying salts — have an action on milk proteins which prevents processed cheese from separating out.

Adverse Effects   There is some suggestion that polyphosphates could cause digestive disturbances by the blocking a number of enzymes.

Typical Products   Cheeses

Under consideration by
the E.E.C. for an 'E'
prefix.

545   Ammonium polyphosphates

Origin   Prepared synthetically.

Function   Emulsifiers; emulsifying salts; curing aids; water-binding aids. Enables manufacturer to add water to frozen chicken.

Adverse Effects   There is some suggestion that polyphosphates could cause digestive disturbances by the blocking a number of enzymes.

Typical Products   Cheeses

Under consideration by
the E.E.C. for an 'E'
prefix.

551   Silicon dioxide (Silicea, Silica)

Origin
Silicon dioxide is the commonest rock-forming mineral and sand is composed mainly of small grains of quartz or flint, both of which are silicon dioxide. In the food industry the grains are further processed into a microcellular powder producing a gel form and a colloidal form by further hydrolysis.

Function
Suspending and anti-caking agent; thickener and stabilizer in suspensions and emulsions, including wine.

Adverse Effects
None known.

Typical Products
Shaped crisps

Under consideration by the E.E.C. for an 'E' prefix.

---

552   **Calcium silicate**

Origin   A naturally occurring mineral. Commercial calcium silicate is prepared synthetically.

Function   Anti-caking agent; in pharmacology as an antacid; glazing, polishing and release agent (sweets); dusting agent (chewing gum); coating agent (rice).

Adverse Effects   None known.

Typical Products

Salt
Garlic and onion salt
Icing sugar
Sweets
Rice
Chewing gum

Under consideration by
   the E.E.C. for an 'E'
   prefix.

553(a)	**Magnesium silicate, synthetic and Magnesium trisilicate**

Origin Magnesium silicate is a synthetic compound of magnesium oxide, and silicon dioxide. Magnesium trisilicate occurs in nature as the minerals meerschaum, parasepiolite and sepiolite.

Function Anti-caking agent and tablet excipient and as an antacid in pharmacology; glazing, polishing and release agent (sweets); dusting agent (chewing gum); coating agent (rice).

Adverse Effects None known.

Typical Products
Salt
Garlic and onion salt
Icing sugar
Sweets
Rice
Chewing gum

Under construction by the E.E.C. for an 'E' prefix.

553(b)   **Talc (French chalk)**

Origin   A naturally occurring mineral, worked in the
                  U.S.A., France, Italy, Canada etc.

Function   Release agent.

Adverse   None known.
Effects

Typical   —
Products
                  Under consideration by
                     the E.E.C. for an 'E'
                     prefix.

554   **Aluminium sodium silicate**

Origin   Naturally occurring mineral, known as analcite
                  and natrolite.

Function   Anti-caking agent.

Adverse   None known.
Effects

Typical   Packet noodles
Products
                  Under consideration by
                     the E.E.C. for an 'E'
                     prefix.

556   Aluminium calcium silicate (Calcium aluminium silicate)

Origin	Naturally occurring mineral, known as scolecite and heulandite.
Function	Anti-caking agent.
Adverse Effects	None known.

Typical Products	—
	Under consideration by the E.E.C. for an 'E' prefix.

558   Bentonite (Bentonitum; Soap clay)

Origin	A particular clay deposit occurring in thin beds in the western U.S.A., believed to result from the decomposition of volcanic ash.
Function	Anti-caking agent; clarifying agent; suspending and emulsifying agent.
Adverse Effects	None known.

Typical Products	—
	Under consideration by the E.E.C. for an 'E' prefix.

559   Kaolin, heavy and Kaolin, light

Origin   Occurs in nature as an altered mineral in granite, particularly in Cornwall, the U.S.A., France, China and Malaya.

Function   Anti-caking agent.

Adverse Effects   None known.

Typical Products   —

Under consideration by the E.E.C. for an 'E' prefix.

570   Stearic acid

Origin   Naturally occurring fatty acid found in all animal fats and vegetable oils. Prepared synthetically for commercial use.

Function   Anti-caking agent.

Adverse Effects   None known.

Typical Products   —

Under consideration by the E.E.C. for an 'E' prefix.

572   **Magnesium stearate**

Origin   Prepared synthetically from commercial stearic acid.

Function   Anti-caking agent; emulsifier; release agent.

Adverse Effects   None are known from the consumption of this additive but accidental inhalation of the powder can be harmful.

Typical Products   Sweets made by direct
        compression

Under consideration by
        the E.E.C. for an 'E'
        prefix.

---

575   **D-Glucono-1,5-lactone, (Glucono *delta*-lactone)**

Origin   Prepared by oxidation of glucose.

Function   Acid; sequestrant. In dairy industry prevents milkstone formation (deposits of magnesium and calcium phosphates etc., when milk is heated to a high temperature); in breweries prevents beerstone formation.

Adverse Effects   None known.

Typical Products   Packet cake mix

Under consideration by
        the E.E.C. for an 'E'
        prefix.

Typical Fish Fingers

E124: Ponceau 4R

E102: Tartrazine

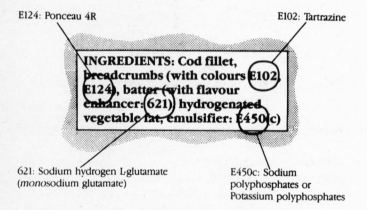

INGREDIENTS: Cod fillet, breadcrumbs (with colours E102, E124), batter (with flavour enhancer: 621) hydrogenated vegetable fat, emulsifier: E450(c)

621: Sodium hydrogen L-glutamate (*mono*sodium glutamate)

E450c: Sodium polyphosphates or Potassium polyphosphates

576   **Sodium gluconate**

Origin   Prepared synthetically; the sodium salt of gluconic acid.

Function   Sequestrant; dietary supplement.

Adverse Effects   None known.

Typical Products   —

Under consideration by
  the E.E.C. for an 'E'
  prefix.

---

577   **Potassium gluconate**

Origin   Prepared synthetically; the potassium salt of gluconic acid.

Function   Sequestrant.

Adverse Effects   None known.

Typical Products   —

Under consideration by
  the E.E.C. for an 'E'
  prefix.

578	**Calcium gluconate**

Origin Prepared synthetically; calcium salt prepared from gluconic acid.

Function Buffer; firming agent; sequestrant.

Adverse Effects None known.

Typical Products —

Under consideration by the E.E.C. for an 'E' prefix.

620	**L-glutamic acid**

Origin A naturally occurring amino-acid of great importance in the nitrogen metabolism of plants and animals, but prepared commercially by the fermentation of a carbohydrate solution by a bacterium e.g. *Micrococcus glutamicus*. Several other methods exist.

Function Dietary supplement; flavour enhancer; salt substitute.

Adverse Effects None known.

Typical Products —

Under consideration by the E.E.C. for an 'E' prefix.

---

621   **Sodium hydrogen L-glutamate
(*mono*Sodium glutamate;
Aji-no-moto; MSG)**

Origin   Occurs naturally in a Japanese seaweed called
Seatango; prepared commercially from sugar beet
pulp and wheat gluten.

Function   Flavour-enhancer of proteinaceous foods either
by increasing the amount of saliva produced in
the mouth or by stimulating the taste buds.

Adverse   Can give rise to a condition known as 'Chinese
Effects   Restaurant syndrome' the symptoms of which are
heart palpitations, headaches, dizziness, muscle
tightening, nausea, weakness of the upper arms,
pains in the neck and symptoms similar to
migraine in some people. Prohibited in or on
foods intended for babies or young children. (See
pages 12-14.)

Typical   Packet snacks
Products   Chilli sauce
Frozen potato waffles
Pork pies
Pork sausages
Packet soup and quick
    soups
Flavoured noodles

Under consideration by
    the E.E.C. for an 'E'
    prefix.

---

622   **Potassium hydrogen L-glutamate (*mono*Potassium glutamate)**

Origin   Prepared synthetically.

Function   Flavour enhancer; salt substitute.

Adverse Effects   Sometimes nausea, vomiting, diarrhoea and abdominal cramps may occur, although there is usually little toxicity of potassium salts when taken by mouth in healthy individuals as potassium is rapidly excreted in the urine. Potassium could be harmful for those with impaired kidneys. Not to be given to babies under 12 weeks old. (See also pages 12-14.)

Typical Products   Sodium-free
                condiments

                Under consideration by
                the E.E.C. for an 'E'
                prefix.

623   **Calcium dihydrogen di-L-glutamate (Calcium glutamate)**

Origin   Prepared synthetically.

Function   Flavour enhancer; salt substitute.

Adverse Effects   None known, but not to be given to babies under 12 weeks old. (See also pages 12-14.)

Typical Products   Dietetic foods

                Under consideration by
                the E.E.C. for an 'E'
                prefix.

627   **Guanosine 5'(disodium phosphate) (Sodium guanylate)**

Origin   The sodium salt of 5' Guanylic acid, a widely-occurring nucleotide (isolated from sardines and yeast extract), prepared synthetically for commercial use.

Function   Flavour-enhancer.

Adverse Effects   None known, but prohibited in or on foods intended for babies or young children. People suffering from conditions such as gout, which require the avoidance of purines are recommended to avoid this substance. (See also pages 12-14.)

Typical Products
Pre-cooked dried rice
    snacks
Crisps
Gravy granules

Under consideration by
    the E.E.C. for an 'E'
    prefix.

---

631   Inosine 5'-(disodium phosphate) (Sodium 5'-inosinate)

Origin

The disodium salt of inosinic acid, (muscle inosinic acid) which can be prepared from meat extract and dried sardines.

Function

Flavour enhancer.

Adverse Effects

None known, but prohibited in or on foods specially made for babies and young children. People suffering from conditions such as gout, which require the avoidance of purines, should avoid this substance. (See also pages 12-14.)

Typical Products

Pre-cooked dried rice
   snacks
Some crisps
Gravy granules

Under consideration by
   the E.E.C. for an 'E'
   prefix.

---

635   Sodium 5'-ribonucleotide

Origin

A mixture of disodium guanylate and disodium inosinate.

Function

Flavour enhancer.

Adverse Effects

None known but not permitted in foods specially prepared for babies or young children. People suffering from conditions such as gout, which require the avoidance of purines, should avoid this substance. (See also pages 12-14.)

---

*Typical
Products*

Frozen croquette
   potatoes
Potato waffles
Mini waffles

Under consideration by
   the E.E.C. for an 'E'
   prefix.

---

636 **Maltol**

Origin

A naturally occurring substance found in the bark
of young larch trees, pine needles, chicory, wood
tars, oils and roasted malt. Also obtained
chemically by alkaline hydrolysis of streptomycin
salts.

Function

Flavouring agent, to impart 'freshly baked' smell
and flavour to bread and cakes.

*Adverse
Effects*

None known.

---

*Typical
Products*

Bread
Cakes

Under consideration by
   the E.E.C. for an 'E'
   prefix.

---

637   **Ethyl maltol**

Origin   Chemically prepared from maltol.

Function   Flavouring, to impart a sweet taste.

Adverse   None known.
Effects

Typical   —
Products

         Under consideration by
          the E.E.C. for an 'E'
          prefix.

---

900 Dimethylpolysiloxane (Simethicone; Dimethicone)

Origin   A chemically manufactured mixture of liquid dimethylpolysiloxane and silica gel or silicon dioxide.

Function   Water repellent; anti-foaming agent.

Adverse Effects   None known.

Typical Products

Jams
Pineapple juice

Products containing dimethylpolysiloxane may also contain formaldehyde in proportion to the additives use up to 1000mg/kg.

Under consideration by the E.E.C. for an 'E' prefix.

---

901   **Beeswax, white and Beeswax, yellow**

Origin   A naturally occurring product from the bee honeycomb. White beeswax is the bleached and purified form.

Function   Glazing and polishing agent, release agent.

Adverse Effects   None known.

Typical Products   Diluents for food
         colours

     Under consideration by
         the E.E.C. for an 'E'
         prefix.

---

903   **Carnauba wax**

Origin   A yellow to light brown wax obtained from the surface of leaves of *Copernicia cerifera*, the Brazilian wax palm.

Function   Glazing and polishing agent for sugar confectionery.

Adverse Effects   None known.

Typical Products   Only permitted in
          chocolate products
          such as in:
Sugar confectionery
Chocolate
          confectionery

Under consideration by
          the E.E.C. for an 'E'
          prefix.

---

904   Shellac

Origin   Shellac is a substance obtained from the resin produced by the Lac insect (*Laccifer lacca,* a member of the *Lacciferidae*) related to mealy bugs and scale insects belonging to the *Coccoidea*. It is a native of India. Four commercial grades are produced by different chemical processes.

Function   Glazing agent.

Adverse Effects   No significant reports of adverse effects.

Typical Products

Cake decorations
Sweets
Fizzy orange drink
Sugar strands

Under consideration by
   the E.E.C. for an 'E'
   prefix.

Mineral Hydrocarbons

905　　　　**Mineral hydrocarbons**

Origin　　　Chemically manufactured mineral derivatives.

Function　　Polishes, glazing agents, sealing agents, ingredient
　　　　　　for chewing gum.

Adverse　　 Excessive dosage may result in anal seepage and
Effects　　　irritation.

Typical　　　Dried fruit (to prevent
Products　　　　sugaring of berries
　　　　　　　　and clouding of film
　　　　　　　　bags)
　　　　　　Citrus fruit
　　　　　　Sugar confectionery
　　　　　　Chewing gum
　　　　　　Cheese rind
　　　　　　Eggs (through dipping
　　　　　　　　or spraying for
　　　　　　　　preserving which
　　　　　　　　must be declared)

　　　　　　Under consideration by
　　　　　　　　the E.E.C. for an 'E'
　　　　　　　　prefix.

---

907   Refined microcrystalline wax

Origin   Prepared by solution of the heavy fraction of petroleum by dewaxing or deoiling methods.

Function   Chewing gum ingredient; polishing and release agent. Also stiffening agent and for tablet coating.

Adverse Effects   None known.

Typical Products   —

Under consideration by
   the E.E.C. for an 'E'
   prefix.

920   L-cysteine hydrochloride and L-cysteine hydrochloride monohydrate

Origin   A synthetically prepared derivative of the naturally occurring amino-acid, cysteine.

Function   Improving agent for flour, other than wholemeal.

Adverse Effects   None known.

Typical Products   Flour and bakery
   products

Under consideration by
   the E.E.C. for an 'E'
   prefix.

924   **Potassium bromate**

Origin   Prepared synthetically.

Function   Oxidizing agent; flour maturing agent; flour bleaching agent.

Adverse Effects   Can cause nausea, vomiting, severe abdominal pain, diarrhoea and even convulsions. Bleaching of flour destroys much of its natural vitamin E and other nutrients and the chemicals used have not all been proved to be completely safe.

Typical Products   Bread

Under consideration by the E.E.C. for an 'E' prefix.

925   **Chlorine**

Origin   Prepared synthetically.

Function   Antibacterial and antifungal preservative; bleaching agent.

Adverse Effects   Powerful irritant. Bleaching of flour has never been demonstrated to be 100 per cent safe. The process takes its toll of flour nutrients and destroys much of the vitamin E content.

Typical Products   Flour

Under consideration by the E.E.C. for an 'E' prefix.

926   **Chlorine dioxide**

Origin   Prepared synthetically.

Function   Bleaching and improving agent for flour; bleaching agent for fats and oils, beeswax etc; purification of water; taste and odour control of water; oxidizing agent; bactericide and antiseptic.

Adverse Effects   Bleaching of flour has never been demonstrated to be 100 per cent safe. It takes its toll of flour nutrients and destroys much of the vitamin E.

Typical Products   Flour

Under consideration by the E.E.C. for an 'E' prefix.

927   **Azodicarbonamide (Azoformamide)**

Origin   Prepared synthetically.

Function   Flour improving agent to improve the tolerance of bread dough under a wide range of fermentation conditions.

Adverse Effects   None known.

Typical Products   Flour

Under consideration by the E.E.C. for an 'E' prefix.

Alphabetical List of Additives and Their 'E' Numbers

E414	Acacia
E260	Acetic acid
E472(a)	Acetic acid esters of mono- and di-glycerides of fatty acids
E472(e)	mono- and diacetyltartaric esters of mono- and di-glycerides of fatty acids
E142	Acid Brilliant Green BS
355	Adipic acid
E406	Agar
621	Aji-no-moto
E405	Alginate ester
E400	Alginic acid
E160(a)	Alpha-carotene
E460	*Alpha*-cellulose
E173	Aluminium
556	Aluminium calcium silicate
554	Aluminium sodium silicate
E123	Amaranth
E440(b)	Amidated pectin
E403	Ammonium alginate
503	Ammonium carbonate
510	Ammonium chloride
380	*tri*-Ammonium citrate
381	Ammonium ferric citrate
381	Ammonium ferric citrate; green
503	Ammonium hydrogen carbonate
527	Ammonium hydroxide
442	Ammonium phosphatides

545	Ammonium polyphosphates
E160(b)	Annatto
E163	Anthocyanins
E300	L-Ascorbic acid
E304	Ascorbyl palmitate
927	Azodicarbonamide
927	Azoformamide
E122	Azorubine
E162	Beetroot Red
901	Beeswax, white
901	Beeswax, yellow
E160(e)	beta-apo-8'-carotenal
E160(a)	alpha-carotene
558	Bentonite
E210	Benzoic acid
E162	Betanin
E320	BHA
E321	BHT
500	Bicarbonate of soda
E230	Biphenyl
E161(b)	Bixin
E151	Black PN
133	Brilliant blue FCF
154	Brown FK
155	Brown HT
E320	Butylated hydroxyanisole
E321	Butylated hydroxytoluene
E263	Calcium acetate
E404	Calcium alginate
E302	Calcium L-ascorbate
E213	Calcium benzoate
E227	Calcium bisulphite
E170	Calcium carbonate
509	Calcium chloride
509	Calcium chloride; anhydrous
E333	*mono*Calcium citrate
E333	*di*Calcium citrate
E333	*tri*Calcium citrate
E238	Calcium formate

578	Calcium gluconate
623	Calcium glutamate
623	Calcium di-hydrogen di-L-glutamate
352	Calcium hydrogen malate
E341(b)	Calcium hydrogen orthophosphate
E540	Calcium hydrogen phosphate
E341(b)	Calcium tetrahydrogen diorthophosphate
529	Calcium oxide
E227	Calcium hydrogen sulphite
526	Calcium hydroxide
E327	Calcium lactate
352	Calcium malate
E341(c)	*tri*Calcium diorthophosphate
540	*di*Calcium diphosphate
544	Calcium polyphosphates
E282	Calcium propionate
552	Calcium silicate
385	Calcium disodium EDTA
385	Calcium disodium ethylenediamine-NNN'N' tetra-acetate
E203	Calcium sorbate
E482	Calcium stearoyl-2-lactylate
516	Calcium sulphate
E226	Calcium sulphite
E161(g)	Canthaxanthin
E160(c)	Capsanthin
E160(c)	Capsorubin
E150	Caramel
E153	Carbon black
E290	Carbon dioxide
E466	Carboxymethylcellulose, sodium salt
E120	Carmine of Cochineal
E120	Carminic acid
E122	Carmoisine
903	Carnauba wax
E410	Carob gum
E160(a)	Carotene, alpha, beta and gamma
E407	Carrageenan

E465	Cellulose, ethyl methyl
E463	Cellulose, hydroxypropyl
E464	Cellulose, hydroxypropylmethyl
E460(i)	Cellulose, microcrystalline
E460(ii)	Cellulose, powdered
925	Chlorine
926	Chlorine dioxide
E140	Chlorophyll
154	Chocolate brown FK
155	Chocolate brown HT
E330	Citric acid
E472(c)	Citric acid esters of mono- and di-glycerides of fatty acids
E472(c)	Citroglycerides
E466	CMC
E120	Cochineal
E124	Cochineal Red A
E461	Cologel
E336	Cream of tartar
E161(c)	Cryptoxanthin
E100	Curcumin
920	L-cysteine hydrochloride
920	L-cysteine hydrochloride monohydrate
E472(e)	Diacetyltartaric acid esters of fatty acids
E333	*di*Calcium citrate
540	*di*Calcium diphosphate
900	Dimethylpolysiloxane
E230	Diphenyl
E340(b)	*di*Potassium hydrogen orthophosphate
E336	*di*Potassium L-(+)-tartrate
E450(a)	*di*Sodium dihydrogen diphosphate
E339(a)	*di*Sodium hydrogen orthophosphate
E335	*di*Sodium L-(+)-tartrate
E312	Dodecyl gallate
542	Edible bone phosphate
442	Emulsifier YN
E127	Erythrosine BS
E160(f)	Ethyl ester of beta-apo-8'-carotenoic acid

E214	Ethyl-4-hydroxybenzoate
E214	Ethyl *para*-hydroxybenzoate
E215	Ethyl-4-hydroxybenzoate, sodium salt
637	Ethyl maltol
E465	Ethylmethylcellulose
E306	Extracts of natural origin rich in tocopherols
E161(a)	Flavoxanthin
E236	Formic acid
553(b)	French chalk
297	Fumaric acid
E160(a)	gamma-carotene
575	Glucono *delta*-lactone
575	D-Glucono-1, 5-lactone
620	L-glutamic acid
E471	Mono- and di-glycerides of fatty acids
E422	Glycerol
E471	Glyceryl monostearate
E197	Gold
E142	Green S
627	Guanosine 5ʹ (disodium phosphate)
E412	Guar gum
E414	Gum Arabic
370	1,4-Heptonolactone
E239	Hexamine
E239	Hexamethylenetetramine
507	Hydrochloric acid
E231	2-Hydroxybiphenyl
E463	Hydroxypropylcellulose
E464	Hydroxypropylmethylcellulose
E464	Hypromellose
E132	Indigo carmine
631	Inosine 5ʹ (disodium phosphate)
E172	Iron hydroxides
E172	Iron oxides
559	Kaolin
416	Karaya gum
154	Kipper Brown
E270	Lactic acid

E472(b)	Lactic acid esters of mono- and di-glycerides of fatty acids
E101	Lactoflavin
E472(b)	Lactoglycerides
478	Lactylated fatty acid esters of glycerol and propane -1, 2-diol
E322	Lecithin
620	L-glutamic acid
E142	Lissamine Green
E180	Lithol Rubine BK
E410	Locust bean gum
E161(b)	Lutein
E160(d)	Lycopene
504	Magnesium carbonate
528	Magnesium hydroxide
530	Magnesium oxide
553(a)	Magnesium silicate synthetic
553(a)	Magnesium trisilicate
572	Magnesium stearate
518	Magnesium sulphate
296	DL-Malic acid, L-Malic acid
636	Maltol
E163	Malvidin
E421	Mannitol
353	Metatartaric acid
E461	Methocel
E461	Methylcellulose
E218	Methyl 4-hydroxybenzoate
E218	Methyl *para*-hydroxybenzoate
E219	Methyl 4-hydroxybenzoate, sodium salt
E460(i)	Microcrystalline cellulose
907	Microcrystalline wax, refined
905	Mineral hydrocarbons
E472(e)	Mono- and diacetyltartaric acid esters of mono- and di-glycerides of fatty acids
E471	Mono- and di-glycerides of fatty acids
E333	*mono*Calcium citrate
E332	*mono*Potassium citrate

622	*mono*Potassium glutamate
E336	*mono*Potassium L-(+)-tartrate
E331	*mono*Sodium citrate
621	*mono*Sodium glutamate
E335	*mono*Sodium L-(+)-tartrate
621	MSG
375	Niacin
375	Nicotinic acid
234	Nisin
E160(b)	Norbixin
570	Octadecarnoic acid
E311	Octyl gallate
E338	Orthophosphoric acid
E231	Orthophenylphenol
E304	6-0-Palmitoyl-L-ascorbic acid
E131	Patent blue V
E440(a)	Pectin
E163	Pelargonidin
E450(b)	*penta*Potassium triphosphate
E450(b)	*penta*Sodium triphosphate
E163	Peonidin
E163	Petunidin
E338	Phosphoric acid
E180	Pigment Rubine
E475	Polyglycerol esters of fatty acids
476	Polyglycerol esters of polycondensed fatty acids of castor oil
476	Polyglycerol polyricinoleate
432	Polyoxyethylene (20) sorbitan monolaurate
433	Polyoxyethylene (20) sorbitan mono-oleate
434	Polyoxyethylene (20) sorbitan monopalmitate
435	Polyoxyethylene (20) sorbitan monostearate
436	Polyoxyethylene (20) sorbitan tristearate
430	Polyoxyethylene (8) stearate
431	Polyoxyethylene (40) stearate
544	Polyphosphates, calcium
545	Polyphosphates, ammonium
E450(c)	Polyphosphates, potassium and sodium
432	Polysorbate 20

434	Polysorbate 40
435	Polysorbate 60
436	Polysorbate 65
433	Polysorbate 80
E124	Ponceau 4R
E261	Potassium acetate
E402	Potassium alginate
E212	Potassium benzoate
924	Potassium bromate
501	Potassium carbonate
508	Potassium chloride
E332	*mono*Potassium citrate
E332	*tri*Potassium citrate
E450(a)	*tetra*Potassium diphosphate
536	Potassium ferrocyanide
577	Potassium gluconate
622	*mono*Potassium glutamate
536	Potassium hexacyanoferrate (II)
501	Potassium hydrogen carbonate
E332	Potassium dihydrogen citrate
622	Potassium hydrogen L-glutamate
E340(a)	Potassium dihydrogen orthophosphate
E340(b)	*di*Potassium hydrogen orthophosphate
E336	Potassium hydrogen tartrate
525	Potassium hydroxide
E326	Potassium lactate
351	Potassium malate
E224	Potassium metabisulphite
E252	Potassium nitrate
E249	Potassium nitrite
E340(c)	*tri*Potassium orthophosphate
E440(a)	Potassium pectate
450(a)	*tetra*Potassium diphosphate
450(b)	*penta*Potassium triphosphate
E450(c)	Potassium polyphosphates
E283	Potassium propionate
E470	Potassium salts of fatty acids

E337	Potassium sodium DL-tartrate
E337	Potassium sodium L-(+)-tartrate
E202	Potassium sorbate
515	Potassium sulphate
E336	*mono*Potassium L-(+)-tartrate
E336	*di*Potassium L-(+)-tartrate
E450(b)	penta Potassium triphosphate
E460(ii)	Powdered cellulose
E405	Propane -1, 2-diol alginate
E477	Propane -1, 2-diol esters of fatty acids
E280	Propionic acid
E405	Propylene glycol alginate
E310	Propyl gallate
E216	Propyl 4-hydroxybenzoate
E216	Propyl *para*-hydroxybenzoate
E217	Propyl 4-hydroxybenzoate, sodium salt
E104	Quinoline yellow
128	Red 2G
907	Refined microcrystalline wax
E161(f)	Rhodoxanthin
E101	Riboflavin
101(a)	Riboflavin-5'-phosphate
E180	Rubine
E161(d)	Rubixanthin
904	Shellac
551	Silica
551	Silicon dioxide
E174	Silver
E262	Sodium acetate
E401	Sodium alginate
541	Sodium aluminium phosphate
E301	Sodium L-ascorbate
E211	Sodium benzoate
500	Sodium bicarbonate
E232	Sodium biphenyl-2-yl oxide
E222	Sodium bisulphite
500	Sodium carbonate
E466	Sodium carboxymethylcellulose
E331	*mono*Sodium citrate

E331	*di*Sodium citrate
E331	*tri*Sodium citrate
E450(a)	*tetra* Sodium diphosphate
E450(a)	*tri*Sodium diphosphate
E215	Sodium ethyl *para*-hydroxybenzoate
535	Sodium ferrocyanide
E237	Sodium formate
576	Sodium gluconate
621	*mono*Sodium glutamate
627	Sodium guanylate
535	Sodium hexacyanoferrate (II)
500	Sodium hydrogen carbonate
E331	Sodium dihydrogen citrate
E262	Sodium hydrogen diacetate
E450(a)	*di*Sodium dihydrogen diphosphate
621	Sodium hydrogen L-glutamate
350	Sodium hydrogen malate
E339(a)	Sodium dihydrogen orthophosphate
E339(a)	*di*Sodium hydrogen orthophosphate
E450(a)	*di*Sodium dihydrogen diphosphate
E222	Sodium hydrogen sulphite
524	Sodium hydroxide
631	Sodium inosinate
E325	Sodium lactate
350	Sodium malate
E223	Sodium metabisulphite
E219	Sodium methyl *para*-hydroxybenzoate
E251	Sodium nitrate
E250	Sodium nitrite
E232	Sodium orthophenylphenate
E339(c)	*tri*Sodium orthophosphate
E440(a)	Sodium pectate
E450(a)	*tri*Sodium diphosphate
E450(a)	*tetra*Sodium diphosphate
E450(b)	*penta*Sodium triphosphate
E450(c)	Sodium polyphosphates
E281	Sodium propionate
E217	Sodium propyl *para*-hydroxybenzoate

635	Sodium 5'-ribonucleotide
E470	Sodium salts of fatty acids
500	Sodium sesquicarbonate
E201	Sodium sorbate
E481	Sodium stearoyl-2-lactylate
514	Sodium sulphate
E221	Sodium sulphite
E335	*mono*Sodium L-(+)-tartrate
E335	*di*Sodium L-(+)-tartrate
E450(b)	*penta* Sodium triphosphate
E200	Sorbic acid
493	Sorbitan monolaurate
494	Sorbitan mono-oleate
495	Sorbitan monopalmitate
491	Sorbitan monostearate
492	Sorbitan tristearate
E420(i)	Sorbitol
E420(ii)	Sorbitol syrup
570	Stearic acid
E483	Stearyl tartrate
363	Succinic acid
E474	Sucroglycerides
E473	Sucrose esters of fatty acids
E220	Sulphur dioxide
513	Sulphuric acid
E110	Sunset yellow FCF
E307	Synthetic *alpha*-tocopherol
E308	Synthetic *beta*-tocopherol
E309	Synthetic *delta*-tocopherol
553(b)	Talc
E334	L-(+)-Tartaric acid
E472(d)	Tartaric acid esters of mono- and di-glycerides of food fatty acids
E102	Tartrazine
E450(a)	*tetra*Potassium diphosphate
E450(a)	*tetra*Sodium diphosphate
E233	Thiabendazole
E171	Titanium dioxide

E307	*alpha*-Tocopherol, synthetic
E309	*delta*-Tocopherol, synthetic
E308	*beta*-Tocopherol, synthetic
E306	Tocopherols, extracts of natural origin
E413	Tragacanth
380	*tri*Ammonium citrate
E333	*tri*Calcium citrate
E341(c)	*tri*Calcium diorthophosphate
E332	*tri*Potassium citrate
E340(c)	*tri*Potassium orthophosphate
E331(a)	*tri*Sodium citrate
E450(a)	*tri*Sodium diphosphate
E339(c)	*tri*Sodium orthophosphate
E153	Vegetable carbon
E161(e)	Violoxanthin
375	Vitamin B
E101	Vitamin B_2
E300	Vitamin C
E306	Vitamin E (natural)
E307	Vitamin E (synthetic)
E308	Vitamin E (synthetic)
E309	Vitamin E (synthetic)
907	Wax, refined, microcrystalline
E415	Xanthan gum
107	Yellow 2G

Glossary of Additive Terms

Acid
Acids are added to foods either to impart a sour or sharp flavour or for technological reasons, to control the level at which other substances in the food can function. The degree of acidity can thus be controlled in jams and preserves to regulate the optimum level of setting that can be achieved by the pectin in the fruit. Substances which neutralize acids are called alkalis or bases such as sodium, calcium and ammonium hydroxide, and substances which can hold the acid-alkali balance at a constant level are known as buffers.

Anti-caking Agents
These are substances which are added to foods such as icing sugar or salt or powdered milk to help them to flow freely and prevent the particles sticking together.

Antifoaming Agents
These are substances added to a food either to prevent excessive frothing on boiling or to reduce the formation of scum or to prevent boiling over. E900 Dimethylpolysiloxane, an inert silicone substance, is an example of an anti-foaming agent.

Antioxidants
Under normal circumstances fats and oils slowly become oxidized when they are exposed to the oxygen in the atmosphere. The process is accompanied by the development of a rancid 'off' flavour which if eaten can cause sickness. The addition of

antioxidants to the fats prevents the process of oxidation. Antioxidants are also added to other non-fat foods such as cut fruits to prevent discolouration brought about by oxidation.

Artificial Sweeteners

These are substances, other than sugar, capable of producing a sweet taste.

Azo dyes

An azo dye has a particular chemical structure of the atoms in its molecule. It could be this 'azo' construction within the molecule to which a proportion of the population is sensitive, or it might be because of impurities. About a fifth of people who are sensitive to aspirin (usually middle-aged adults and more commonly women than men) are also sensitive to azo dyes. Other groups which may be affected are asthmatics and people who suffer from eczema.

The kinds of reactions that occur in sensitive people are contractions of the bronchi — the tubes allowing air into the lungs — (and asthmatic attacks), nettle rash, watering eyes and nose, blurred vision, swelling of the skin with fluid and in extreme cases shock and reduction in blood platelets with the production in the blood of anti-platelet antibodies. (The blood platelets are involved in blood clotting to seal wounds.)

It has been suggested by the late Dr Ben Feingold that azo dyes are among those substances which could trigger off the hyperactivity syndrome in children (see pages 12-14). The following are azo dyes:

E102   Tartrazine
E107   Yellow 2G
E110   Sunset yellow FCF
E122   Carmoisine
E123   Amaranth
E124   Ponceau 4R
E128   Red 2G
  154   Brown FK
  155   Chocolate brown HT

E151   Black PN
E180   Pigment rubine

'Coal tar dye' is an old name — it means nowadays that the dye is synthetically made and doesn't occur in nature. It would include all the above plus:

E104   Quinoline yellow
E127   Erythrosine
E131   Patent blue V
E132   Indigo carmine
E133   Brilliant blue FCF

Bases

Bases are added to foods to increase their alkalinity or reduce their acidity. Sometimes they are added to react with acids to give off carbon dioxide gas for aerating purposes.

Bleaching Agents

Substances employed to artificially bleach and whiten flour.

Buffers

Buffers are chemical substances which can resist considerable changes in the acid/alkali balance of solutions. The scale along which acid or alkali levels are measured is called the pH. Buffers (usually salts of weak acids) can maintain the pH at a predetermined level despite the addition of further acid or alkali.

Bulking Aids

Food additives which add to the bulk of the food but do not add to the calorific or energy value. The bulking aids are of value in slimming foods but they also help to 'pad out' or simulate more expensive ingredients.

Chelating Substances

When the acid/alkali ratio exceeds a particular limit or the ratio of traces of metal to one another exceeds a particular level, the trace metals may be precipitated out. The addition of a chelating substance such as EDTA (E385) retains the trace elements in the food solution, by bonding them on to an amino acid.

Coal Tar Dye
See azo dye.

Colour Index (C.I.) Numbers
These colour reference numbers are allocated in the Colour-Index of the Society of Dyers and Colourists (3rd Edition with 1975 revisions).

Colouring Matters
Water- or oil-soluble substances (or insoluble substances) which are produced artificially or are naturally occurring. Sometimes the colouring is permitted only on the outside of foods especially confectionery but usually it is permitted throughout the food.

Diluents
Substances which are used to dilute other additives or to dissolve them.

Emulsifiers
These are substances which can bring together oil, which is water-hating (hydrophobic) and water which is lypophobic (fat-hating) and mix them so that they do not separate out into layers. Some emulsifiers are plant gums, some are chemicals and others are synthetically produced derivatives of natural products.

Emulsifying Salts
A mixture of salts such as citrates, phosphates and tartrates which is added to cheese when it is melted as part of its processing to prevent the 'stringiness' which normally happens when cheese is cooked.

Excipients
This is normally a pharmacological term for 'inactive' powdered substances which are used to bind an 'active' drug into a tablet. The term is also applied in the baking industry to denote a carrier substance for additives used in bread.

220

Firming Agents

Calcium and magnesium salts are employed to retain the natural firmness or crispness of fruits and vegetables and to prevent their softening during the processing period.

Flavour Modifiers or Enhancers

These are substances used to enhance or reduce the taste or smell of a food without imparting any flavour of their own, so they are not 'flavours' as such, neither are they enzymes.

Gelling Agents

Substances which are capable of forming a jelly. Many of the gelling agents may be used in a stabilizing capacity too but not all stabilizers are capable of setting into a jelly.

Glazing Agents

Substances which either provide a shiny appearance or polish to the food or provide a protective coat, or both.

Humectants

These are substances which absorb water vapour from the atmosphere and prevent the food from drying out and becoming hard and unpalatable. Glycerine is added to royal icing in the home as a humectant, to prevent the icing drying out and hardening.

Liquid Freezants

Liquids or liquefiable gases which can freeze food by coming into contact with it directly and extracting heat from it.

Mineral Hydrocarbons

A wide variety of substances derived from bitumen (paraffin hydrocarbons) whether liquid, semi-liquid or solid. The group includes white oil, liquid paraffin, petroleum jelly, microcrystalline wax and hard paraffin.

Packaging Gases

These are inert gases which are employed to occupy space in packaging which if occupied by atmospheric air would cause oxidation of the contents or encourage the growth of micro-organisms.

Preservatives

Preservatives are substances which inhibit the growth of bacteria, fungi and viruses within foods and thus prevent the spoilage of these foods. Gases such as sulphur dioxide, organic and inorganic acids, phosphates and nitrates are all preservatives.

Propellants

Gases or volatile liquids employed in aerosol containers to expel the contents when the button is depressed.

Release Agents

Substances added to the machinery or coated onto food to prevent foods from sticking to the surfaces of food-processing equipment such as moulds, conveyors, cooking pans or trays. Release agents such as magnesium stearate are also added to tins in which foods are packaged to allow the contents to slip out easily.

Sequestrants

Traces of metals, always present in the environment, can cause deterioration in food by advancing the oxidation process, or cause premature setting in dessert mixes. Sequestrants are substances capable of attaching themselves to the trace metals such as calcium, iron or copper.

Solvents

These are liquids which are used to disperse substances either in solution or in suspension. They may also be used for extraction, then can either remain, as can be the case with the alcoholic extraction of a flavour, or be removed, as when oil is dissolved from seed.

Stabilizers

Similar in function to emulsifiers and thickeners, stabilizers serve to protect the droplets in an emulsion from collision with one another and consequently their tendency to separate out.

Stabilizers reduce coalescence either by adding to the viscosity or thickness of the medium forming a protection to the droplets or by forming protective colloids so the frequency and energy of collisions are minimized. The term 'stabilizer' may embrace thickening and gelling agents.

Synergists

A synergist is a substance which is capable of increasing or enhancing the effect of another substance. In the context of food additives, synergists are usually used to enhance the effects of antioxidants. These synergists include tartaric and citric acid and their calcium potassium and sodium salts.

Thickeners

Food additives which add to the viscosity of a food. Most of the thickeners employed are of plant origin, for example, seaweed or algae derivatives or substances produced from cellulose capable of forming a gel or colloid. Silicon dioxide (551) is the only inorganic additive employed as a thickener.

Vitamins

Most vitamins are not regarded as food additives unless they are fulfilling the function of a food additive such as that of antioxidant in the case of E300 L-Ascorbic acid (vitamin C) or E306-9 Tocopherols (vitamin E) or a colour in the case of 101a Riboflavin-5'-phosphate (vitamin B_2).

E FOR ADDITIVES SUPERMARKET SHOPPING GUIDE

PART II
'ADDITIVE SAFE' SUPERMARKET SHOPPING GUIDE

CONTENTS

PUBLISHER'S NOTE

The information given in this book has been compiled from questionnaires sent to supermarkets and, whilst every effort has been made to ensure the accuracy of this information, the publisher cannot be held responsible for any errors of fact or changes in formulation, so please read the label.

INTRODUCTION

The Industrial Revolution brought with it the easy availability of fine white flour, plentiful supplies of sugar and the processing of foods. A new food law brought in controls not too different from those we have today which included the provision that food has to be safe. The difficulty is knowing what is safe. So far as additives are concerned, it was not until the 1950s that consumption and demand began to grow at a rapid rate, with consumers demanding less and less preparation time but ever cheaper products and manufacturers looking for ways to supply. If you buy a pound of sausages for 75p then you have to ask yourself how a manufacturer can use good meat when that costs around twice as much. He *has* to incorporate water, fat and cereals plus flavours and colours to produce a palatable and attractive product at the right price.

In 1970, food labelling regulations made manufacturers declare what sorts of additives were being used but without any detail. So a substance listed as 'preservatives' could be a benzoate (such as E211) which can adversely affect asthmatics or those sensitive to aspirin, or another naturally derived substance such as sorbic acid (E200) found in the berries of the Mountain Ash. The Common Market has changed all that. Now all additives other than flavours and one or two exempt categories have to be declared with either E numbers or the full names of the substance together with the use to which it is put, such as colour or anti-oxidant (to prevent rancidity or browning). This is a substantial consumer freedom of information and enables us to decide, provided we arm ourselves with sufficient knowledge, just what we eat. Ever since this law was announced food manufacturers and retailers have been looking closely again at the recipes they use and are making modifications where it is felt that the public will find it difficult to accept a particular additive. Another consequence of this is, of course, that the consumer may have to be prepared to pay more for a food with a shorter shelf life and with more expensive ingredients.

The Austrian wine scandal in 1985 highlighted the fact that there were more than 15 permitted additives in EEC wines and because none of them have to be declared in alcoholic drinks, Public Health Inspectors have paid scant attention to analysing just what is in them. The anti-freeze was not discovered simply because no-one looked for it. It is ironic that an Austrian VAT Inspector found the additive was being claimed in substantial quantities for a production rebate and alerted the authorities. Analysts will now be paying much more attention to what we drink and I am sure that this will have the dual effect of safeguarding us and at the same time turning up more mysterious additions.

All additives have to be declared in descending order and so the position of, for example, sugar and salt on the label tells its own message. However, in alcoholic drinks where there are no declarations you may not be aware that a sweet vermouth can contain almost 16 per cent sugar, port 12 per cent and liqueurs such as cherry brandy over 30 per cent. Coca-cola by comparison has only 10.5 per cent.

Almost everything we do in life has a potential risk and a potential benefit. You have to decide in your own situation the risks and the benefits of the various groups of additives and of individual substances within them. It is certainly more useful to preserve meat products than it is to allow the growth of some of the most toxic bacteria known. None of us want our foods to go off, but there is often a choice as to the means of achieving this. A meat pie can be preserved

8

against rancidity with vitamin E (E306) or you can use the more questionable E320 and E321 (BHA and BHT). Another example is vitamin C (E300), which is very effective for preventing deterioration of many foods.

A good question to ask yourself when reading a food label is 'would I use this in the kitchen, and if not, why is it used here?' A snack product I examined recently had 13 E numbers, none of which I would have used at home. Why were there so many colours and other additives, such as E320 and E321, which are not permitted for foods intended for babies and young children, in a product that could be eaten by them so frequently? It would be a useful step forward if there was an obligatory flash saying 'contains ingredients not recommended for babies'. A reduction of the additives in use to about one-third of their present number would bring about visible and widespread changes to the appearance, texture and taste of many of the foods we eat but would avoid the risk in susceptible individuals of problems such as hyperactivity in children, asthma, nettle rash, eczema and tummy upsets whilst giving us foods much nearer those we would like to have time to make at home. Meanwhile we can become more selective in our eating styles and, above all, enjoy a healthy diet that is varied and full of interest.

The first British health food store store opened as long ago as 1894 and today you can obtain from them many interesting and exciting foods without unnecessary additives. However, the high-street supermarkets and food stores now also provide a selection which has been carefully produced to avoid these additions, which is what the Guide is all about.

Since the consumer-led revolution demanding food with fewer additives began in the autumn of 1984, the high-street supermarkets and food stores have not been slow to react in providing the sort of food required by the selective and well-informed customer. Safeway, Tesco, Sainsbury's, Waitrose, The Co-op, Marks and Spencer and many more all have definite, consumer-oriented policies on foods which, although they may take some time to implement, allow us to choose from a steadily increasing number of excellent foods with reduced and carefully thought-out additives.

In order to compile the Guide, I selected 79 named additives that I would personally prefer to do without which represent 56 different substances. In doing so, I did not mean to imply that they were dangerous, but simply that the selected additives have either been shown to be quite unnecessary, like many of the colours, or can cause adverse reactions in certain sensitive people. Others enable the manufacturer to produce expensive-looking food from cheap raw materials. Most of the major retailers in the UK were asked to list all their products which did *not* contain any of these additives. At the same time they recorded the amount of added salt and sugars in each item. This information has been used to create this guide, giving you a quick and easy means of cutting down on contentious additives and at the same time keeping an eye on your intake of salt and sugars. The full list of excluded additives is given below. If a product contains one of these in its listed ingredients, it should not be in this book. However, we have had to rely on the accuracy of the contributors, so if you are determined to avoid all exposure to certain additives, you must check the label.

The Excluded Additives

E102 Tartrazine	E124 Ponceau 4R
E104 Quinoline yellow	E127 Erythrosine BS
107 Yellow 2G	128 Red 2G
E110 Sunset yellow FCF	E131 Patent blue V
E120 Carmine of	E132 Indigo carmine
Cochineal	133 Brilliant blue
E120 Carminic acid	FCF
E120 Cochineal	E142 Acid Brilliant Green
E122 Azorubine	BS
E122 Carmoisine	E142 Green S
E123 Amaranth	E142 Lissamine Green

E150	Caramel	E220	Sulphur dioxide
E151	Black PN	E221	Sodium sulphite
E153	Carbon black	E222	Sodium bisulphite
E153	Vegetable carbon	E222	Sodium hydrogen sulphite
154	Brown FK	E223	Sodium metabisulphite
154	Chocolate brown FK		
154	Kipper Brown	E224	Potassium metabisulphite
155	Brown HT		
155	Chocolate brown HT	E226	Calcium sulphite
E173	Aluminium	E227	Calcium bisulphite
E180	Lithol Rubine BK	E250	Sodium nitrite
E180	Pigment Rubine	E251	Sodium nitrate
E210	Benzoic acid	E310	Propyl gallate
E211	Sodium benzoate	E311	Octyl gallate
E212	Potassium benzoate	E312	Dodecyl gallate
E213	Calcium benzoate	E320	BHA
E214	Ethyl-4-hydroxybenzoate	E320	Butylated hydroxyanisole
E214	Ethyl para-hydroxybenzoate	E321	BHT
		E321	Butylated hydroxytoluene
E215	Ethyl-4-hydroxy-benzoate, sodium salt	385	Calcium disodium EDTA
E216	Propyl 4-hydroxy-benzoate	385	Calcium disodium ethylenediamine-NNN'N' tetra-acetate
E216	Propyl para-hydroxybenzoate		
E217	Propyl 4-hydroxy-benzoate, sodium salt	E407	Carrageenan
		621	Aji-no-moto
		621	monoSodium glutamate
E218	Methyl 4-hydroxy-benzoate		
		621	MSG
E218	Methyl para-hydroxybenzoate	621	Sodium hydrogen L-glutamate
E219	Methyl 4-hydroxy-benzoate, sodium salt	622	monoPotassium glutamate

622	Potassium hydrogen L-glutamate	631	Inosine 5' (disodium phosphate)
623	Calcium disodium EDTA	635	Sodium 5'-ribonucleotide
623	Calcium di-hydrogen di-L-glutamate	924	Potassium bromate
623	Calcium glutamate	925	Chlorine
627	Guanosine 5' (disodium phosphate)	926	Chlorine dioxide

Many people have spent a lot of time and trouble filling in detailed forms in order to be included in this book. Others have reasons for not participating. For example, some companies have a rapid turnover of the types of food available, consequently they could not be sure that the products mentioned would be available even a few months after writing. Others felt that their development programmes were not sufficiently advanced to be sure that products which they intended to change would be ready in time for publication. We hope to bring out revised editions of the Guide at regular intervals so that more and more of these can be included as time goes on.

The attitude of the Food Manufacturers Federation is by no means as positive as that of the supermarket chains. They wrote to their members on 10 October, 1985, suggesting that this guide was not the type of initiative with which reputable companies would readily associate themselves without a considerable amount of further clarification. They also said 'the basic principle would seem to be that if a manufacturer determines to produce a product without the use of food additives — especially as a replacement for an existing product — he should not promote it by stating or suggesting that the new product is thereby inherently safer, or the old one inherently more dangerous.' Sainsbury does not seem to have been too impressed because they took a full page advertisement in *The Daily Telegraph* on 12 November, 1985, headlined *No Fishy Ingredients:* 'Our new fish fingers are 100 per cent cod fillet, batter and breadcrumbs and there are no artificial preservatives or colourings. No polyphosphates. No tartrazine. Of course to your kids they'll just be good old fish fingers. Only you will know how good they really are. Good food costs less at Sainsbury's.'

Other supermarket chains and manufacturers have taken the same step: it makes good marketing sense to them and provides excellent products for you and me. The great problem has been to know in a quick and easy way just what foods have been made with the consumer's view of additives in mind. So this guide, with the co-operation of producers and suppliers, sets out to be a convenient, quick and easy reference book to help you plan a diet low in additives.

HOW TO USE THE GUIDE

This guide contains an alphabetic listing of supermarket and high street store own-brand products which do not contain the additives listed on pages 10-12. Each supermarket's list is preceded (where available) by a statement of their policy towards additives. Each entry gives the name of the product followed by a salt, sugars and flavourings rating, and finally the packaging method (this is included so that you can distinguish between things like frozen and canned peas).

None of the products listed should contain any of our excluded additives, but if you or your children are very sensitive to particular ones, it is as well to double check with the label. It is also important to remember that there are many excellent products which are eligible for inclusion in the Guide, but which are not here for some reason; they were too late to make the print date, or they are new products, for example. So if you see something you like the look of, check the label against our additive list. Fresh meat, fish, poultry, eggs, vegetables and fruit have not been included unless they have been pre-prepared, as in such things as kebabs or stir-fry vegetables, where additives *may* have been used.

Salt
The zero, low and high categories for added salt (sodium chloride) are designed to be a useful quick check of salt levels, they should *not* be used as a guide for people on special diets, because the element sodium can be present

in many forms and, indeed, occurs naturally in a lot of foods. So if you are on a low sodium diet, the best thing to do is to write to the manufacturer to find out just how much total sodium there is in a particular food. On the other hand, if you wish to cut down your salt intake a little or not eat foods that have a lot added, then zero means that none has been put there by the manufacturer, low (L) means that there is 1 per cent or less and high (H) that there is more than 1 per cent. The letter X denotes this information is not available. Such a figure needs to be interpreted with common sense; for example, how much of the product are you actually going to use? A few drops of sauce or flavouring containing a relatively high quantity of salt is unlikely to add much to the diet, whereas a high figure for a staple food such as a breakfast cereal could make a significant difference. Nevertheless, there is much argument over whether salt has a harmful affect on a normal person with little general agreement among nutritionists.

Sugars
Many foods contain added sugars such as sucrose, maltose, glucose etc. Sugar is another additive which some consumers would prefer to eat less of, although it has to be noted that many foods contain large quantities of natural sugars — around 70 per cent in honey, for example. Sugars added by the manufacturer may be there as a preservative or to give flavour and 'feel' in the mouth. Foods containing no added sugars are listed with a zero symbol, 5 per cent or less added sugars is classed as low (L) and more than 5 per cent as high (H). The letter X denotes this information is not available.

Flavourings
The Common Market Commission is hoping to produce a list of food flavours, many of which are already derived from natural substances, but at the moment there is no way of identifying added flavours, all we have been able to do is

identifying added flavours, all we have been able to do is note their presence or absence. The letter F denotes the presence of flavouring, and the figure 0 means there is no added flavouring. We cannot trace any substantial bad effects coming from commonly used flavours.

Hidden Additives
There is no legal requirement to include additives such as preservatives or flour improvers to the list of ingredients if they have no effect on the product as a whole and are only incorporated into one or other of the ingredients. Thus the apple flakes in your muesli may be preserved naturally or artificially and there is no way of telling from the ingredients list. So we have *not* asked contributors to declare such additives. This would present great difficulties, especially as a fluctuation in the supply of raw materials could mean that one batch had a very small additive content and others did not. One thing you can be sure of, however, is that the total amount present would be very small.

The additive-conscious buyer also needs to watch out when buying alcoholic drinks, because here the manufacturers do not have to declare additives at all. In fact there is a permitted list for table wines within the Common Market, but only the manufacturer knows precisely what has been used. With these provisos, we are sure that this guide will be of great use to the health-conscious shopper.

The book *E For Additives* was the parent of this guide. Its publication breaks new ground for the consumer and we look forward to hearing constructive suggestions from retailers, manufacturers and readers so that successive editions become ever more useful.

The Boots Company PLC

Boots has for many years sold a wide range of foods, including baby and diabetic foods.

In more recent years, as the role of diet in promoting and maintaining good health has increasingly been recognised, our product range has been expanded. We now have over 200 foodcentres open in larger Boots branches where we aim to encourage healthy eating through:

— Products that both taste good and offer nutritional value.
— Providing consumers with full nutritional information in-store and on our product labels.

In our Boots brand food range we are already working on the removal of all additives associated with allergic reaction in some people or not positively contributing to the product's final quality and value.

We already have a wide range of products, for instance the Boots Second Nature range, that contain no artificial colours, flavours, or preservatives.

For all new Boots brand products we also aim to avoid the use of any artificial additive. This will not always be possible. For example, preservatives are necessary in many soft drinks to prevent the risk of contamination. Their removal poses a particular problem because acceptable alternatives are not currently available. However, as a minimum, no new product will contain any artificial colour or flavour.

At the same time, we believe that the subject of additives should not be treated in isolation to the wider need of providing nutritionally balanced foods, including all aspects of ingredient contents such as sugar, fat and fibre level. The other essential requirement is that the product should taste good.

It is also important that consumers are provided with sufficient information in making their choice. With this in mind, we are progressively incorporating a 'Food Facts' panel on our labels which gives nutritional information and has a statement, where appropriate, on the inclusion of artificial additives.

BOOTS	Salt	Sugar	Flavour	Packaging
Acid drops	O	H	F	bag
Apple juice, fresh pressed English	O	O	O	tetrapak
Apple juice, pure	O	O	O	tetrapak
Apple pie, wholemeal	L	H	O	
Baby Foods				
Apple & sultana dessert	O	H	O	dried
Apple dessert	O	H	O	jar
Banana hazelnut treat	O	H	O	dried
Beef casserole	O	H	O	dried
Beef dinner	O	O	O	dried
Breakfast porridge oats	O	O	O	dried
Cauliflower cheese	O	L	O	dried
Cheese & tomato savoury	O	O	O	dried
Cheese savoury	O	O	O	jar
Cheese supper	O	O	O	jar
Chicken dinner	O	O	O	dried
Chicken supper	O	O	O	jar
Chocolate dessert	O	H	O	jar
Chocolate pudding	O	H	O	jar
Country chicken casserole	O	O	O	jar
Country vegetable bake	O	H	O	dried

BOOTS	Salt	Sugar	Flavour	Packaging
Egg & cheese savoury	0	L	0	dried
Egg custard	0	H	0	dried
English breakfast	0	L	0	dried
Lamb casserole	0	0	0	jar
Lamb dinner	0	0	0	dried
Lamb hotpot	0	0	0	jar
Lamb hotpot	0	L	0	dried
Liver & bacon casserole	0	0	0	jar
Liver & bacon dinner	0	0	0	jar
Minced beef & vegetables	0	0	0	jar
Mixed cereal breakfast	0	0	0	dried
Mixed cereal with wholewheat & wheatgerm	0	H	0	dried
Mixed fruit dessert	0	H	0	jar
Mixed fruit salad	0	H	0	jar
Mixed vegetable savoury	0	0	0	jar
Oat breakfast	0	H	0	dried
Orchard apple pudding	0	H	0	jar
Pear dessert	0	H	0	jar
Pear treat dessert	0	H	0	jar
Pineapple & banana dessert	0	H	0	dried
Porridge oats with malt	0	H	0	dried

BOOTS	Salt	Sugar	Flavour	Packaging
Protein baby cereal	O	O	O	dried
Rice pudding with rosehips	O	H	O	dried
Rice, baby	O	O	O	dried
Ruskmen	O	H	O	
Rusks	O	H	O	
Rusks, apricot flavour, low sugar	O	H	F	
Rusks, low sugar	O	L	O	
Savoury beef noodles	O	L	O	dried
Savoury chicken & rice	O	L	O	dried
Savoury chicken casserole	O	H	O	dried
Savoury mixed vegetables	O	O	O	dried
Savoury vegetable casserole	O	O	O	jar
Scrambled egg breakfast	O	O	O	dried
Steak & kidney casserole	O	H	O	dried
Tropical fruit treat	O	H	O	dried
Yogurt dessert, rosehip & raspberry	O	H	O	dried
Yogurt dessert, strawberry & orange	O	H	O	dried
Baking powder	O	H	O	
Basting sauce for chicken (Fine Foods)	H	H	O	
Basting sauce for lamb (Fine Foods)	L	H	O	
Basting sauce for peppered beef (Fine Foods)	H	H	O	

BOOTS	Salt	Sugar	Flavour	Packaging
Beans, borlotti	L	L	0	can
Beans, butter	L	L	0	can
Beans, haricot	L	L	0	can
Beans, red kidney	L	0	0	can
Beef & vegetable casserole	0	0	0	jar
Biscuits, apple (Second Nature)	L	H	F	
Biscuits, fruit bran (Second Nature)	L	H	F	
Biscuits, hand baked coconut & honey	L	H	0	
Biscuits, hand baked fig and orange	L	H	0	
Biscuits, hand baked ginger & lemon	L	H	0	
Biscuits, hand baked sultana & bran	L	H	0	
Biscuits, hazelnut (Second Nature)	L	H	0	
Biscuits, muesli fruit (Second Nature)	L	H	F	
Biscuits, sesame seeds (Second Nature)	L	H	0	
Biscuits, six grain (Second Nature)	L	H	F	
Biscuits, wheat (Second Nature)	L	H	0	
Biscuits, wholewheat honey (Second Nature)	L	H	F	
Blackcurrant drink, ready to drink	0	H	0	tetrapak
Blackcurrant flavour liquid centre drops	0	H	F	bag
Bran flakes, with sultana & apple	H	H	0	
Bran, unprocessed (Second Nature)	0	0	0	

BOOTS	Salt	Sugar	Flavour	Packaging
Bread, country grains	L	O	O	
Bread, muesli	L	L	O	
Bread, wholemeal	L	O	O	
Breakfast cereal, bran	H	H	O	
Cake, sultana & carrot	L	H	O	
Cereal mix, country (Vegetarian)	L	O	O	carton
Chick peas	L	L	O	can
Conserve, apricot (Fine Foods)	O	H	O	
Conserve, black cherry (Fine Foods)	O	H	O	
Conserve, blackcurrant (Fine Foods)	O	H	O	
Conserve, raspberry (Fine Foods)	O	H	O	
Conserve, strawberry (Fine Foods)	O	H	O	
Country casserole (Vegetarian)	L	L	F	alum tray in carton
Crispbread, whole rye (Shapers)	H	L	O	
Crunch bar, coconut (Second Nature)	O	H	O	
Crunch bar, oat & honey (Second Nature)	O	H	O	
Dessert sauce, caramel with brandy (Fine Foods)	O	H	F	
Dessert sauce, chocolate with rum (Fine Foods)	O	H	O	
Dessert sauce, raspberry with kirsch (Fine Foods)	O	H	O	
Diabetic biscuit, ginger cream	O	O	F	
Diabetic biscuit, hazelnut	L	L	O	

BOOTS	Salt	Sugar	Flavour	Packaging
Diabetic biscuit, muesli	L	L	F	
Diabetic biscuit, tea	L	O	F	
Diabetic cake mix, chocolate sandwich	O	O	O	
Diabetic cake mix, plain sandwich	O	O	O	
Diabetic chocolate drink	L	O	F	
Diabetic milk chocolate	O	H	F	
Diabetic milk chocolate with hazelnut	O	H	F	
Diabetic mint imperials	O	O	O	
Diabetic peaches, Reduced Calorie	O	O	O	can
Diabetic pears, Reduced Calorie	O	O	O	can
Diabetic plain chocolate	O	H	F	
Diabetic spread, honey	O	H	O	
Doughnuts, wholemeal	L	H	O	
Fruit & nut milk chocolate, diet (Shapers)	O	H	F	
Glucose powder with vitamin C	O	O	O	
Grapefruit juice, unsweetened	O	H	O	tetrapak
Hazelnut milk chocolate, diet (Shapers)	O	H	F	
Lasagne (Second Nature)	O	O	O	
Lasagne, vegetable (Vegetarian)	L	L	O	
Lentil mix, Farmhouse (Vegetarian)	H	O	O	alum tray in carton
Macaroni (Second Nature)	O	O	O	carton

BOOTS	Salt	Sugar	Flavour	Packaging
Malted drink	L	H	O	
Marmalade, orange with thin cut peel (Fine Foods)	O	H	O	bag
Menthol liquid centre drops, traditional	O	H	F	
Milk chocolate, diet (Shapers)	O	H	F	
Muesli milk chocolate, diet (Shapers)	O	H	F	
Muesli, fruit & nut, deluxe	O	O	O	
Muesli, honey (Second Nature)	O	H	O	
Muesli, no added sugar (Second Nature)	O	O	O	
Mustard, Dijon with mixed herbs (Fine Foods)	H	O	O	
Mustard, English with beer & garlic (Fine Foods)	H	O	O	
Nut mix, harvest (Vegetarian)	H	O	O	carton
Orange juice, unsweetened	O	O	O	tetrapak
Pasties, vegetable	L	O	O	
Peaches, Reduced Calorie (Shapers)	O	O	O	can
Pears, Reduced Calorie (Shapers)	O	O	O	can
Plain chocolate, diet (Shapers)	O	O	F	
Poppyseed bar	O	H	O	
Porridge, hi-fibre (Second Nature)	O	H	O	
Ratatouille (Vegetarian)	O	O	O	
Reduced Calorie food snack, cheese & chive flavour	O	O	F	alum tray in carton

BOOTS	Salt	Sugar	Flavour	Packaging
Reduced Calorie food snack, cheese & ham flavour	O	O	F	
Reduced Calorie food snack, cheese flavour	O	O	F	
Rice, brown (Second Nature)	O	O	O	alum tray in carton
Risotto, vegetable (Vegetarian)	L	L	O	
Rolls, country grains	L	L	O	
Rolls, wholemeal	L	O	O	
Savoury spread	H	L	O	
Scones, wholemeal	O	H	O	
Sesame seed bar	O	H	O	
Shortbread, wholemeal (Second Nature)	L	O	O	
Soup, mixed vegetable with spice (Second Nature)	L	O	O	
Soup, thick green bean (Second Nature)	L	O	O	
Soup, thick potato (Second Nature)	L	O	O	
Spaghetti (Second Nature)	O	H	O	
Sunflower seed bar	O	O	O	
Vegetable curry (Vegetarian)	L	O	O	alum tray in carton
Vegetable sausage mix (Vegetarian)	H	O	O	carton
Water, sparkling spring	O	O	O	bottle
Wheatgerm, stabilised (Second Nature)	O	O	O	

NOTES

NOTES

BHS®
BRITISH HOME STORES PLC

BRITISH HOME STORES	Salt	Sugar	Flavour	Packaging
Almonds	L	O	O	dried
Apple & sultana cake, with buttercream	L	H	O	pre-packed
Bacon, Ayrshire middle	H	O	O	pre-packed
Beanfeast	O	O	O	dried
Beans, red kidney	O	O	O	dried
Beef Chop Suey ready meal	L	L	O	frozen
Biscuits, carob chip crunch bar	L	H	O	pre-packed
Biscuits, honey & almond cookie	L	H	O	pre-packed
Biscuits, honey wafer	L	H	O	pre-packed
Biscuits, muesli cookie	L	H	O	pre-packed
Biscuits, oat & coconut cookie	L	H	O	pre-packed
Biscuits, round shortcake	L	H	F	pre-packed
Biscuits, Scottish oatcakes	H	O	O	pre-packed
Biscuits, sesame seed & raisin	L	H	O	pre-packed
Biscuits, wheaten	L	H	O	pre-packed
Biscuits, wholewheat, Nature's Snack	X	X	X	pre-packed
Bran	O	O	O	pre-packed
Bratwurst, traditional German	H	L	O	
Breakfast cereal, bran crunch with apple	L	H	X	pre-packed
Breakfast cereal, honey crunch	O	X	X	pre-packed
Breakfast cereal, malted crunch	H	O	X	pre-packed

BRITISH HOME STORES	Salt	Sugar	Flavour	Packaging
Bubble & squeak	H	0	0	pre-packed
Butter, English. unsalted	L	0	0	pre-packed
Buttered whole Brazil nuts	X	X	0	pre-packed
Cauliflower cheese ready meal	L	0	0	pre-packed
Cheese, Appenzell	X	X	X	
Cheese, Bellshire	X	X	X	
Cheese, blue Brie	0	0	0	pre-packed
Cheese, blue Brie, West German	H	0	0	
Cheese, blue Cheshire	X	X	X	
Cheese, blue Stilton	H	0	0	loose
Cheese, blue Stilton	0	0	0	pre-packed
Cheese, blue Wensleydale	X	X	X	
Cheese, Brie	H	0	0	loose
Cheese, Brie	0	0	0	pre-packed
Cheese, Brie with mushrooms	X	X	X	
Cheese, Caerphilly	X	X	X	
Cheese, Camembert	X	X	X	
Cheese, Cheddar with pickle	X	X	X	
Cheese, Cheddar, Canadian	X	X	X	
Cheese, Cheddar, Cathedral City	X	X	X	
Cheese, Cheddar, English extra matured	X	X	X	

BRITISH HOME STORES	Salt	Sugar	Flavour	Packaging
Cheese, Cheddar, English matured	X	X	X	
Cheese, Cheddar, English mild with chives & onion	X	X	X	
Cheese, Cheddar, English with walnuts	X	X	X	
Cheese, Cheddar, Irish	X	X	X	
Cheese, Cheddar, New Zealand extra matured	H	0	0	loose
Cheese, Cheddar, New Zealand medium	H	0	0	loose
Cheese, Cheddar, processed slices	H	0	0	pre-packed
Cheese, Cheddar, Scottish	X	X	X	
Cheese, Cheddar, Scottish matured	X	X	X	
Cheese, Cheddar, Somerset cider	X	X	X	
Cheese, Cheddar, tasty	X	X	X	
Cheese, Cheddar, traditional farmhouse	X	X	X	
Cheese, Cheddar, vegetarian	X	X	X	
Cheese, Cheddar, West Country farm	X	X	X	
Cheese, Cheddar, West Country farmhouse	X	X	X	
Cheese, Cheshire	X	X	X	
Cheese, Cheshire, English	X	X	X	
Cheese, chèvre blanche	X	X	X	
Cheese, Colette	X	0	X	
Cheese, Danish blue	H	0	0	

BRITISH HOME STORES	Salt	Sugar	Flavour	Packaging
Cheese, Danish blue crème	X	X	X	
Cheese, Danish blue, Xtra creamy	X	X	X	
Cheese, Danslot gateaux	L	L	0	loose
Cheese, Dolcelatte	X	X	X	
Cheese, Doux de Montagne	X	X	X	
Cheese, Scottish Highland choice, Dunlop with Drambuie & almonds	X	X	X	
Cheese, Scottish Highland Hebridean, Dunlop with mustard & chive	X	X	X	
Cheese, double Gloucester with chives & onion	X	X	X	
Cheese, Emmental	X	X	X	
Cheese, French Folie du Chef	X	X	X	
Cheese, Fropain des Manges	X	X	X	
Cheese, German smoked processed	X	X	X	
Cheese, German smoked processed with ham	X	X	X	
Cheese, Gruyere	X	X	X	
Cheese, Jarlsberg	X	X	X	
Cheese, Lancashire	X	X	X	
Cheese, Lymeswold	X	X	X	
Cheese, Melbury	X	X	X	
Cheese, Port Salut	X	X	X	

BRITISH HOME STORES	Salt	Sugar	Flavour	Packaging
Cheese, pizza style	X	X	X	
Cheese, Rambol with herbs	X	X	X	
Cheese, Rolalp	X	X	X	
Cheese, Rosette	X	X	X	
Cheese, Roulé	X	X	X	
Cheese, Roulette	X	X	X	
Cheese, red Cheshire	O	O	O	pre-packed
Cheese, red Leicester	X	X	X	
Cheese, red Leicester	O	O	O	pre-packed
Cheese, Samsoe	H	O	O	loose
Cheese, St Albray	X	X	X	
Cheese, sage Derby	X	X	X	
Cheese, Tendale	X	X	X	
Cheese, Tête de Moine	H	O	O	loose
Cheese, white Stilton	L	L	O	frozen
Chicken & mushroom ready meal	H	L	O	chilled
Chilli con Carne ready meal	O	H	O	chilled
Chocolate crème pot	O	H	O	
Chocolate mint leaves	X	X	F	
Chocolate stem ginger	X	X	X	
Coconut macaroons	L	H	F	pre-packed

BRITISH HOME STORES	Salt	Sugar	Flavour	Packaging
Cod in parsley sauce (& veg) ready meal	H	O	O	chilled
Coffee crisp chocolates	X	H	O	
Coffee log	X	X	X	
Coleslaw	L	L	O	chilled
Cornish pasties, 4 large	L	L	O	frozen
Coronation chicken ready meal	O	O	O	chilled
Country cake	O	H	F	
Courgette bake ready meal	L	O	O	chilled
Cream, thick double	O	O	O	
Crispbreads, rye, extra thin	L	O	O	pre-packed
Crisps, cheese & onion flavour	H	O	F	
Crisps, ready salted	H	O	F	
Crisps, smokey bacon flavour	H	O	F	
Crumble, apple & blackberry	L	H	O	frozen
Crumble, plum & almond	L	H	O	frozen
Custard creams	L	H	F	
Digestive milk chocolate biscuits	L	H	O	
Digestive plain chocolate biscuits	L	H	O	
Digestive sweetmeal biscuits	L	H	O	
Duckling à l'orange ready meal	L	L	O	frozen
Éclairs, assorted	X	X	F	

BRITISH HOME STORES	Salt	Sugar	Flavour	Packaging
Éclairs, hazelnut	L	H	F	
Éclairs, milk chocolate	X	X	F	
Egg custard & nutmeg dessert	O	H	O	chilled
Figs, Lerida	O	O	O	pre-packed
Flour, 100% wholemeal	O	O	O	
Fromage blanc, apricot	L	L	O	chilled
Fromage blanc, strawberry	L	L	O	chilled
Fruit jellies	X	X	X	
Fruit salad, fresh	O	O	O	chilled
Fudge fingers	X	X	F	
Hash browns, American style	H	O	O	chilled
Hazelnut fudge cake	L	H	L	
Hazelnuts	L	O	O	
Lemon fudge cake	L	H	L	
Lentils, green	O	O	O	
Liqueur chocolate drum, assortment	X	H	O	pre-packed
Liqueur chocolates, Irish cream	X	H	O	
Milk chocolate Brazils	X	X	X	
Milk chocolate caramels	L	H	O	pre-packed
Milk chocolate crisp	X	X	X	
Milk chocolate fudge fingers	X	X	F	

BRITISH HOME STORES	Salt	Sugar	Flavour	Packaging
Milk chocolate hazelnut whirls	X	H	O	
Milk chocolate honeycomb	X	X	F	
Milk chocolate log	X	X	X	
Milk chocolate truffles	X	X	F	
Milk, pasteurised whole	O	O	O	
Milk, semi-skimmed	O	O	O	
Milk, skimmed	O	O	O	
Mint crisp chocolates	X	H	O	
Mint imperials	X	X	F	
Muesli, Swiss style	O	O	X	pre-packed
Nuts, cashews salted	H	O	O	pre-packed
Nuts, mixed	L	O	O	pre-packed
Orange & apricot drink	O	H	O	chilled
Orange crisp chocolates	X	H	O	
Orange juice, pure	O	O	O	chilled
Oranges in caramel	L	H	O	chilled
Party snacks (peanuts, cashews & sesame sticks)	L	O	F	
Peanut kernels, unsalted	O	H	O	
Peanuts & raisins	O	O	O	
Peanuts, large roasted	H	O	O	
Peanuts, large salted	L	O	O	

BRITISH HOME STORES	Salt	Sugar	Flavour	Packaging
Pie, beefsteak & vegetable	L	O	O	chilled
Pie, chicken & vegetable	L	O	O	chilled
Pie, individual chicken & mushroom	L	O	O	frozen
Pineapple juice, pure	O	L	O	chilled
Pizza, cheese & tomato	H	L	O	chilled
Pizza, deep fill tomato & cheese	L	H	F	chilled
Plain chocolate mint/coffee creams	L	O	O	
Potato bake ready meal	L	O	O	chilled
Potato croquettes	L	O	O	frozen
Potato croquettes	L	O	O	chilled
Quiche Lorraine	H	O	O	loose
Quiche Lorraine	H	O	O	chilled
Quiche Lorraine, 4	L	O	O	frozen
Quiche, asparagus & corn	L	O	O	loose
Quiche, cheese & onion	L	O	O	loose
Quiche, cheese & onion	H	O	O	chilled
Quiche, cheese & onion	L	O	O	chilled
Ratatouille	X	X	F	
Real fruit centres	L	O	O	
Rice, long-grain brown	L	H	O	
Rich tea biscuits	L	O	O	
Rum & raisin log	X	X	X	frozen

BRITISH HOME STORES	Salt	Sugar	Flavour	Packaging
Salads, party	L	L	O	chilled
Smoked haddock au gratin ready meal	H	O	O	chilled
Spaghetti, wholewheat	O	O	O	
Stollen	X	X	X	
Sugar, dark Muscovado	O	H	O	
Sugar, Demerara	O	H	O	
Sugar, light Muscovado	O	H	O	
Toffees, assorted	X	X	F	
Toffees, traditional butter	L	H	F	
Truffle log	X	X	X	
Tsatsiki	L	O	O	chilled
Vegetable curry ready meal	L	O	O	chilled
Vegetable medley ready meal	H	O	O	chilled
Wheatgerm	X	O	O	
Wholewheat pasta & broccoli ready meal	L	O	O	chilled
Wholewheat pasta Mexicalli	L	O	O	chilled
Yogurt, black cherry	O	H	O	
Yogurt, creamy, banana & apricot	O	O	O	
Yogurt, creamy, exotic fruits	O	O	F	
Yogurt, English garden fruits	O	H	F	
Yogurt, natural set	O	O	O	

BRITISH HOME STORES	Salt	Sugar	Flavour	Packaging
Yogurt, natural unsweetened	O	O	O	
Yogurt, thick & fruity apricot & mango	O	H	F	
Yuletide log	X	X	X	

NOTES

NOTES

Budgen

Budgen's position within this now widely debated and controversial arena is characterized above all by a lack of marketing superficiality. We are fully conversant with most of the issues involved and we will continue to keep abreast of trends both from the manufacturers' side and also in terms of monitoring shifts in consumers' buying patterns. We do not, however, believe it appropriate at this stage of the awareness building programme, where information and misinformation vie almost side by side with each other through various channels of media, to evolve yet another spurious 'information package' for consumers on healthy eating.

We would rather leave this kind of information to more expert voices, and offer our customers a more enlightened guide on diet only when the contention of the present issues has been largely resolved and a more balanced view pertains. We are, however, actively engaged in pursuing a superior formulation for our own-label products where necessary.

For some time now we have taken due cognizance of the potentially detrimental effects of certain food additives and have been discussing alternatives with our suppliers on a low-key basis. We have now accelerated this aspect of our supplier dialogue and are undergoing a complete range review which has already, and will increasingly, result in either an additive-free product specification or an 'acceptable' formulation as defined by prevailing standards. It should be pointed out, moreover, that we are indirectly promoting an enhanced diet

45

with our own label range through an increasing product development emphasis towards very lightly processed chilled foods or fresh foods.

Consistent with the growing propensity for many consumers to be appraised with the nutritional composition of the foodstuffs they purchase, Budgen have embarked upon a relabelling exercise to update any historically launched products which did not contain this information. Needless to say it is a prime requirement of any new product launches that they conform to consumer expectations, wherever possible.

BUDGEN	Salt	Sugar	Flavour	Packaging
Apple juice	O	O	O	tetrapak
Baps, brown wholemeal	H	L	O	
Baps, floured	H	L	O	
Baps, soft	H	L	O	
Barley, pearl	O	O	O	can
Beans, baked	H	L	O	can
Beans, butter, dried	X	O	O	frozen
Beans, green, cut	O	O	O	
Beans, green, sliced	O	O	O	
Beans, haricot, dried	O	O	O	
Beans, red kidney, dried	L	H	F	
Biscuits, bourbon creams	L	H	O	
Biscuits, digestive	L	H	O	
Biscuits, rich tea	H	L	O	
Bread, wholemeal loaf	L	L	O	
Breakfast bisk	O	O	O	
Brussels sprouts	H	L	O	frozen
Buns, sesame	L	O	O	
Butter	O	O	O	
Carrots, baby	L	O	O	frozen
Carrots, sliced	L	O	O	can

BUDGEN	Salt	Sugar	Flavour	Packaging
Carrots, whole	L		O	can
Cauliflower florets	O	O	O	frozen
Cheese spread	O	O	O	
Cheese, Caerphilly	H	O	O	
Cheese, Cheshire	H	O	O	
Cheese, Cheddar	H	O	O	
Cheese, cottage, all types	O	O	O	
Cheese, Derby	H	O	O	
Cheese, double Gloucester	H	O	O	
Cheese, Leicester	H	O	O	
Cheese, Stilton, blue	H	O	O	
Cheese, Stilton, white	H	O	O	
Cheese, Wensleydale	H	O	O	
Chips, oven	O	O	O	frozen
Chips, straight cut	O	O	O	frozen
Coffee granules, premium	O	O	O	
Coffee granules, select blend	O	O	O	
Coffee powder, instant	O	O	O	
Coffee, Brazilian Blend	O	O	O	
Coffee, Continental freeze dried	O	O	O	
Coffee, decaffeinated freeze dried	O	O	O	

BUDGEN	Salt	Sugar	Flavour	Packaging
Coffee, French blend	O	O	O	
Coffee, special choice	O	O	O	
Cornflakes	H	H	O	
Croissants	H	L	O	
Crumpets	H	L	O	
Custard creams	L	H	O	
Ginger nuts	L	H	F	
Grapefruit juice	O	O	F	tetrapak
Honey, Australian, clear	O	O	O	
Honey, Australian, set	O	O	O	
Honey, blended, clear	O	O	O	
Honey, blended, set	O	O	O	
Honey, Mexican, clear	O	O	O	
Honey, Mexican, set	O	O	O	
Lentils	O	O	O	
Macaroni, short cut	O	O	O	
Margarine	O	O	O	
Margarine, supersoft	L	L	O	
Marmalade, thick cut	L	H	O	
Milk, semi-skimmed	O	O	O	
Milk, skimmed	O	O	O	

BUDGEN	Salt	Sugar	Flavour	Packaging
Milk, whole	O	O	O	
Muesli	L	H	O	
Oil, corn	O	O	O	
Oil, olive	O	O	O	
Oil, sunflower	O	O	O	
Oil, vegetable	O	O	O	
Orange juice	O	O	O	tetrapak
Peas	O	O	O	frozen
Peas, dried	O	O	O	
Peas, minted	O	O	O	frozen
Peas, yellow split	O	O	O	
Pie, chicken & mushroom	H	L	O	frozen
Pizza, cheese & onion	L	L	O	frozen
Pizza, cheese & tomato	L	L	O	frozen
Pizza, ham & mushroom	L	L	O	frozen
Rice, brown	O	O	O	
Rice, easy cook	O	O	O	
Rice, flaked	O	O	O	
Rice, ground	O	O	O	
Rice, long-grain	O	O	O	
Rice, pudding	O	O	O	

BUDGEN	Salt	Sugar	Flavour	Packaging
Rolls, long	H	L	O	
Rolls, white Scotch	H	L	O	
Semolina	O	O	O	
Shorties	L	H	F	
Spaghetti	O	H	O	
Tapioca, seed pearl	O	O	O	
Tea bags	O	O	O	
Tea, choice	O	O	O	
Tomato purée	O	O	O	
Vegetables, mixed	L	O	O	frozen
Vegetables, mixed	O	O	O	can
Vinegar, red wine	L	O	O	
Vinegar, white wine	O	O	O	
Wholemeals, milk chocolate	O	H	O	
Wholemeals, plain chocolate	L	H	O	

NOTES

carrefour limited

CARREFOUR	Salt	Sugar	Flavour	Packaging
Beans in tomato sauce	H	H	F	
Beetroot, pickled	H	L	O	
Breakfast biscuits	L	L	O	
Brown sauce	H	H	F	
Cabbage, pickled	H	L	O	
Carrots	H	L	O	can
Coffee creamer	H	H	O	
Cream crackers	H	L	O	
Crisps	H	O	O	
Donuts, jam	L	H	F	
Fruit juices, all varieties	O	O	F	
Jams, all varieties	X	H	O	
Margarine	H	L	O	
Margarine, sunflower oil	H	L	O	
Marmalades, all varieties	X	H	O	
Milk, dried	O	O	O	
Milk, fresh	O	O	O	
Mincemeat	X	H	F	
Muesli	O	L	O	
Oil, cooking	O	O	O	
Oil, sunflower	O	O	O	

54

CARREFOUR	Salt	Sugar	Flavour	Packaging
Onions, pickled	H	L	O	
Peas	O	O	O	frozen
Peas, garden	H	L	F	can
Peas, processed	H	L	F	can
Potatoes	X	O	O	can
Rice pudding	O	L	O	can
Rice, long-grain	H	O	O	
Salad dressing	O	H	F	
Soft drinks, all varieties	O	H	F	
Soft drinks, carbonated	O	H	F	
Soft drinks, low calorie	O	L	F	
Spaghetti	H	H	F	can
Sweet mixed pickle	H	H	F	
Table jellies	O	H	F	
Tomato ketchup	H	H	F	
Vinegar	O	O	O	

NOTES

FINE FARE

FINEFARE	Salt	Sugar	Flavour	Packaging
Almonds, blanched	0	0	0	packet
Almonds, flaked	0	0	0	loose
Almonds, flaked	0	0	0	packet
Almonds, ground	0	0	0	loose
Almonds, ground	0	0	0	packet
Apple juice, pure	0	X	0	tetrapak
Apple slices, dried	0	X	0	dried, pack your own
Apricot halves in fruit juice	0	H	0	can
Apricot halves in syrup	0	H	0	can
Barley, pearl	0	0	0	packet
Bay leaves	X	X	X	loose/dried
Beachcomber mix	L	L	F	loose
Beans in tomato sauce	H	0	F	can
Beans with sausages in tomato sauce	0	0	0	can
Beans, butter, dried	0	L	0	loose
Beans, butter, dried	L	L	0	packet
Beans, curried	H	0	F	can
Beans, in tomato sauce	0	0	0	can
Beans, mung, dried	0			loose
Beans, pinto, dried	0			loose

FINEFARE	Salt	Sugar	Flavour	Packaging
Beans, red kidney	H	L	0	can
Beans, red kidney, dried	0	0	0	loose
Beans, red kidney in chilli sauce	H	L	0	can
Beans, sliced green	0	0	0	frozen
Beans, whole green	0	0	0	frozen
Beef grillsteaks	L	0	0	frozen
Biscuits, all-butter thins	L	L	F	packet
Biscuits, bourbon creams	L	L	F	packet
Biscuits, digestive (Yellow Pack)	L	H	0	packet
Biscuits, milk chocolate wheatmeal	L	H	0	packet
Biscuits, plain chocolate ginger	L	H	0	packet
Biscuits, plain chocolate wheatmeal	L	H	0	packet
Biscuits, rich tea (Yellow Pack)	L	H	0	packet
Biscuits, wheatmeal half-coated milk chocolate flavour (Yellow Pack)	L	H	F	packet
Biscuits, wheatmeal, half-coated plain chocolate flavour (Yellow Pack)	L	H	F	packet
Blackberries in syrup	0	H	F	can
Bouquet garni	0	0	0	dried
Bread mix, wholemeal	X	X	X	
Brussels sprouts	0	0	0	frozen

59

FINEFARE	Salt	Sugar	Flavour	Packaging
Butter, pure dairy	H	O	O	packet
Caramel wafers, fully coated	L	H	F	packet
Carrots, sliced in salted water	H	O	O	can
Carrots, whole baby	O	O	O	frozen
Carrots, whole in salted water	H	O	O	can
Carrots, young baby in salted water	H	O	O	can
Cauliflower florets	O	O	O	frozen
Cheese & ham nibbles	H	O	F	packet
Cheese spread	X	O	O	tub
Cheese, cottage with onions & chives	L	O	O	fresh
Cheese, cottage with pineapple	L	O	O	fresh
Cheese, cottage, natural	L	O	O	fresh
Chick peas, dried	O	L	O	loose
Chicken portions, sage & onion flavour	L	O	O	fresh
Chicken spread	H	O	O	jar
Chips, oven	O	O	O	frozen
Chips, straight cut	O	O	O	frozen
Chives, dried	O	O	O	packet
Chocolate chip cookies	L	H	O	packet
Chocolate eclairs	L	H	F	loose
Chocolate eclairs	L	H	F	packet

FINEFARE	Salt	Sugar	Flavour	Packaging
Citrus fruit drink	O	H	O	tetrapak
Cocoa	L	L	O	loose
Cocoa	O	L	F	packet
Coconut crumble creams	L	L	F	packet
Coconut macaroons	L	H	O	packet
Coconut, desiccated	O	L	O	packet
Coconut, sweetened tenderized	O	H	O	packet
Cod fillets, plain	O	O	O	frozen
Cod fillets, skinless	O	O	O	frozen
Cod in butter sauce	H	X	O	frozen
Cod in parsley sauce	H	X	O	frozen
Coffee & chicory, instant	O	O	O	jar
Coffee beans, breakfast	O	O	O	loose
Coffee beans, Continental	O	O	O	loose
Coffee granules, instant	O	O	O	jar
Coffee granules, instant	O	O	O	jar
Coffee powder, instant	O	O	O	loose
Coffee powder, instant	O	O	O	jar
Coffee powder, instant (Yellow Pack)	O	O	O	jar
Coffee powder, instant	O	O	O	packet
Coffee, instant, gold seal freeze-dried	O	O	O	jar

FINEFARE	Salt	Sugar	Flavour	Packaging
Cooking fat, blend 'n' bake	O	O	O	packet
Corn on the cob	O	O	O	frozen
Cornflakes	L	H	O	packet
Cornish wafers	H	L	O	packet
Cream crackers	H	L	O	packet
Cream crackers (Yellow Pack)	H	X	O	packet
Cream, double	O	O	O	fresh
Cream, double	O	O	O	frozen
Cream, half, pour over sterilized	O	O	O	can
Cream, single	O	O	O	fresh
Cream, sterilized	O	O	O	can
Cream, whipping	O	O	O	fresh
Cream, whipping	O	O	O	frozen
Crisps, cheese & onion	H	X	F	packet
Crisps, ready salted	H	X	O	packet
Crisps, salt & vinegar	H	X	F	packet
Crunchy oat breakfast cereal	L	H	O	packet
Currants	O	H	O	pack your own
Currants	O	H	O	packet
Curry powder	H	O	O	loose/dried

FINEFARE	Salt	Sugar	Flavour	Packaging
Drinking chocolate	H	H	0	loose
Drinking chocolate	L	H	0	packet
Drinking chocolate	L	H	0	can
Finger wafers, fully coated	L	H	F	packet
Fish paste	H	X	0	jar
Flan case	X	X	F	packet
Frutychoc	L	H	F	loose
Garlic salt	H	0	0	loose/dried
Ginger nuts	L	H	0	packet
Ginger thins	L	L	0	packet
Gooseberries in syrup	0	H	0	can
Grapefruit juice, pure	0	0	0	tetrapak
Grapefruit segments in fruit juice	0	H	0	can
Grapefruit segments in light syrup	0	H	0	can
Grapefruit segments, broken, in light syrup	0	H	0	can
Haddock fillets, plain	0	0	0	frozen
Haddock fillets, skinless	0	0	0	frozen
Herbs, mixed, dried	0	0	0	loose
Herbs, mixed, dried	0	0	0	packet
Honey, Australian clear	0	0	0	jar
Honey, Canadian clover set	0	0	0	jar

FINEFARE	Salt	Sugar	Flavour	Packaging
Honey, clear	O	O	O	jar
Honey, Mexican clear	O	O	O	jar
Honey, set	O	O	O	jar
Honeycomb crunch bars	L	H	O	packet
Hot Calypso	X	X	X	loose
Irish stew	H	X	F	can
Jaffa cakes	L	H	O	packet
Jaffa cakes, 18 (Yellow Pack)	L	H	F	packet
Lentils	O	O	O	packet
Lentils, whole light green	O	O	O	loose
Macaroni, short cut	O	O	O	packet
Macaroni, short cut (Yellow Pack)	O	O	O	packet
Malted drink	L	H	O	jar
Malted wholewheat flakes with banana	L	H	O	loose
Malted wholewheat flakes with vinefruit	L	H	O	loose
Marjoram, dried	O	O	O	loose
Mayonnaise, lemon	L	L	F	jar
Mayonnaise, real	L	L	F	jar
Meatballs in tomato sauce	L	L	O	can
Meringue mix	X	X	X	can
Milk, evaporated	O	X	O	can

FINEFARE	Salt	Sugar	Flavour	Packaging
Milk, instant	0	0	0	dried
Mint, dried	0	0	0	loose
Mint, dried	L	0	0	packet
Mint lumps	L	H	0	loose
Mints, sparkling	L	H	0	loose
Mints, sparkling	L	H	0	packet
Mintychoc	L	H	F	loose
Morning bran	L	H	0	packet
Muesli	L	H	0	loose
Muesli breakfast cereal	L	H	0	packet
Muesli, wholefood	L	H	0	packet
Mushrooms, sliced	L	0	0	can
Mushrooms, whole	L	0	0	can
Nice biscuits (Yellow Pack)	L	H	0	packet
Nuts, cashews, roast salted	H	0	0	packet
Nuts, mixed chopped	0	0	0	loose
Nuts, mixed chopped	0	0	0	packet
Nuts, mixed, roast salted	H	X	0	packet
Oatcakes, bran	H	L	0	packet
Oatcakes, traditional	H	L	0	packet
Oatmeal, medium	0	0	0	packet

FINEFARE	Salt	Sugar	Flavour	Packaging
Oil, corn,, pure	O	O	O	bottle
Oil, olive	O	O	O	bottle
Oil, sunflower, pure	O	O	O	bottle
Oil, vegetable, pure	O	O	O	bottle
Oil, vegetable, pure (Yellow Pack)	O	O	O	bottle
Oil, vegetable, pure solid	O	O	O	packet
Onions, dried	O	O	O	loose
Orange juice, pure	O	O	O	tetrapak
Parsley, dried	O	O	O	loose
Parsley, dried	L	H	O	packet
Peanut butter, crunchy	L	H	O	jar
Peanut butter, smooth	X	H	O	jar
Peanuts & raisins	X	L	O	packet
Peanuts, carob coated	H	X	O	loose
Peanuts, large roast salted	H	X	O	packet
Peanuts, roasted salted	X	X	O	packet
Peanuts, yogurt covered	O	O	X	loose
Peas	O	O	O	frozen
Peas, dried	O	O	O	packet
Peas, green split	O	O	O	packet
Peas, mint	O	O	O	frozen

FINEFARE	Salt	Sugar	Flavour	Packaging
Peas, yellow split	O	O	O	packet
Pepper, whole black	O	O	O	loose/dried
Pepper, whole white	O	O	O	loose/dried
Petits pois	O	H	O	frozen
Pie filling, apple	O	H	O	can
Pineapple chunks in syrup	O	O	O	can
Pineapple juice, pure	O	H	O	tetrapak
Pineapple pieces in syrup	O	H	O	can
Pineapple slices in fruit juice	O	H	O	can
Pineapple slices in syrup	H	L	F	can
Pizza, ham & mushroom	H	L	O	frozen
Pizza, onion & cheese, individual	H	L	O	frozen
Pizza, tomato & cheese	H	L	O	frozen
Pizza, tomato & cheese, family	H	L	O	frozen
Pizza, tomato & cheese, individual	H	L	O	frozen
Pizza, tomato & cheese, snack	O	L	O	frozen
Plaice fillets, skinless	H	O	O	frozen
Poppy & sesame seed crackers	O	O	O	packet
Porridge oats	H	O	O	packet
Potatoes, new	H	O	O	can
Prunes, dried	O	H	O	can

FINEFARE	Salt	Sugar	Flavour	Packaging
Prunes in syrup	O	H	O	can
Puffed wheat	L	L	O	packet
Raisins, carob coated	X	L	O	loose
Raisins, seedless	O	H	O	dried, pack your own
Raisins, seedless	O	H	O	dried
Raisins, yogurt covered	X	X	X	loose
Ratatouille	H	H	O	can
Relish, hamburger	H	H	O	jar
Rice pudding	L	H	O	can
Rice, brown	O	O	O	loose
Rice, brown	O	O	O	packet
Rice, easy cook	O	O	O	packet
Rice, ground	O	O	O	packet
Rice, pudding	O	O	O	packet
Rice, short grain	O	O	O	loose
Riceys	L	H	O	loose
Riceys	L	H	O	loose
Rich shorties	L	H	F	packet
Rosemary, dried	O	O	O	loose
Sage, dried	O	O	O	loose

FINEFARE	Salt	Sugar	Flavour	Packaging
Sage, dried	O	O	O	can
Salmon, pink	H	O	O	can
Salmon, red	H	O	O	loose
Salt, cooking	H	O	O	packet
Salt, cooking	H	O	O	packet
Salt, table	L	O	O	can
Sardines in tomato sauce	L	X	O	can
Sardines in vegetable oil	O	X	O	packet
Semolina	L	O	O	
Shortcake	H	H	F	can
Sild in edible oil	H	O	O	can
Sild in tomato sauce	L	O	O	packet
Snowballs	H	H	F	loose
Soup mix, quick	O	H	O	packet
Spaghetti	O	O	O	packet
Spaghetti (Yellow Pack)	H	O	O	can
Spaghetti in tomato sauce (Yellow Pack)	H	L	O	can
Spaghetti in tomato sauce	H	L	F	can
Spaghetti rings in tomato sauce	L	L	F	can
Sponge pudding, treacle	H	X	F	can
Stuffing, parsley & thyme	H	O	O	loose

FINEFARE	Salt	Sugar	Flavour	Packaging
Stuffing, sage & onion	H	O	O	loose
Stuffing, sage & onion	H	O	O	packet
Sweetcorn	O	O	O	frozen
Sweetcorn	H	L	O	can
Tapioca, seed pearl	O	O	O	packet
Tea	O	O	O	packet
Tea	O	O	O	loose
Tea, choice selection	O	O	O	packet
Tea, strong original	O	O	O	packet
Tea bags	O	O	O	packet
Tea bags (Yellow Pack)	O	O	O	packet
Tea bags, choice selection	O	O	O	box
Tea bags, strong original	O	O	O	box
Thyme, dried	O	O	O	loose
Thyme, dried	L	H	F	packet
Toffee whirls	L	H	F	packet
Toffee, dairy	L	O	O	loose
Toffees, creamy	L	H	O	packet
Tomato juice, pure	H	O	O	tetrapak
Tomato purée			O	jar
Trail mix	X	X	X	loose

FINEFARE	Salt	Sugar	Flavour	Packaging
Tropical fruit drink	O	H	O	tetrapak
Tuna in brine	H	O	O	can
Tuna in oil	H	O	O	can
Tuna, skipjack in oil	L	X	O	can
Twigsnacks	H	O	O	packet
Vegetable broth mixture	O	O	O	packet
Vegetables, mixed	O	O	O	frozen
Vegetables, mixed (Yellow Pack)	H	O	O	frozen
Vegetables, mixed	O	O	O	can
Vegetables, stewpack	O	O	O	frozen
Vegetables, stir fry	L	O	O	frozen
Vegetables, supreme mixed	H	O	O	can
Viking pie	O	O	O	frozen
Walnut pieces	L	O	O	loose
Water, soda	L	H	O	bottle
Wheatflakes	H	L	O	packet
Wheatmeal crackers	O	O	O	packet
Whiting fillets, plain	L	H	O	frozen
Wholewheat breakfast cereal biscuits	L	O	O	packet
Yogurt, natural set	O	O	O	fresh

NOTES

HOLLAND & BARRETT

HOLLAND & BARRETT	Salt	Sugar	Flavour	Packaging
Aduki burger, vegetarian	L		O	pre-packed
Alfalfa seeds	O	O	O	bag
Almonds, flaked	O	O	O	bag
Almonds, ground	O	O	O	bag
Almonds, split	O	O	O	bag
Apple rings	O	O	O	bag
Apricots	O	O	O	bag
Banana, dried	O	O	O	bag
Barley flakes	O	O	O	bag
Barley, pot	O	O	O	bag
Bean mix	O	O	O	bag
Beans, aduki	O	O	O	bag
Beans, black eye	O	O	O	bag
Beans, butter	O	O	O	bag
Beans, field	O	O	O	bag
Beans, flageolet	O	O	O	bag
Beans, haricot	O	O	O	bag
Beans, mung	O	O	O	bag
Beans, pinto	O	O	O	bag
Beans, red kidney	O	O	O	bag
Beans, soya	O	O	O	bag

HOLLAND & BARRETT	Salt	Sugar	Flavour	Packaging
Bran	o	o	o	bag
Brazils	o	o	o	bag
Breadcrumbs, wholewheat	o	o	o	bag
Buckwheat	o	o	o	bag
Buckwheat, roast	o	o	o	bag
Cashew pieces	o	o	o	bag
Cashews	o	o	o	bag
Chestnuts, dried	o	o	o	bag
Chick peas	o	o	o	bag
Coconut	o	o	o	bag
Coffee granules, decaffeinated	o	o	o	jar
Corn, popping	o	o	o	bag
Cous cous	o	o	o	bag
Currants	o	o	o	bag
Dates	o	o	o	bag
Figs	o	o	o	bag
Flour, buckwheat	o	o	o	bag
Flour, maize	o	o	o	bag
Flour, soya	o	o	o	bag
Hazelnuts	o	o	o	bag
Hazelnuts, ground	o	o	o	bag

HOLLAND & BARRETT	Salt	Sugar	Flavour	Packaging
Honey, pure blended				jar
Lasagne, wholewheat			○	carton
Lentils, Continental	○	○	○	bag
Lentils, red	○	○	○	bag
Lentils, whole green	○	○	○	bag
Macaroni, wholewheat	○	○	○	bag
Millet	○	○	○	bag
Millet flakes	○	○	○	bag
Muesli	○	○	○	bag
Muesli, high fibre	○	○	○	bag
Nuts & raisins	○	○	○	bag
Nuts, mixed	○	○	○	bag
Nuts, mixed chopped	○	○	○	bag
Peaches, dried	○	○	○	bag
Peanuts	○	○	○	bag
Pears, dried	○	○	○	bag
Peas, green split	○	○	○	bag
Peas, yellow split	○	○	○	bag
Prunes	○	○	○	bag
Prunes, large, ready to eat	○	○	○	bag
Prunes, pitted	○	○	○	bag

HOLLAND & BARRETT	Salt	Sugar	Flavour	Packaging
Pumpkin seeds	0	0	0	bag
Quiche, broccoli & low fat cheese	L	0	0	pre-packed 6 inch
Quiche, courgette & low fat cheese	L	0	0	pre-packed 6 inch
Quiche, vegetarian Cheddar & mixed peppers	L	0	0	pre-packed 6 inch
Raisins, large seeded	0	0	0	bag
Raisins, seedless	0	0	0	bag
Rice, long grain brown	0	0	0	bag
Rice, short grain brown	0	0	0	bag
Rye flakes	0	0	0	bag
Salad, fruit	L	0	0	bag
Samosas, vegetarian	0	0	0	pre-packed
Semolina	0	0	0	bag
Sesame seeds	0	0	0	bag
Soup mix	0	0	0	bag
Spaghetti, wholewheat	0	0	0	bag
Sultanas	0	0	0	bag
Sunflower seeds	0	0	0	bag
Vine fruit, mixed	0	0	0	bag
Walnut halves	0	0	0	bag
Walnut pieces	0	0	0	bag
Wheat	0	0	0	bag

HOLLAND & BARRETT	Salt	Sugar	Flavour	Packaging
Wheat flakes	O	O	O	bag
Wheat, bulgar	O	O	O	bag
Yogurt, apricot, raw sugar	O	H	O	plastic pot
Yogurt, banana, sugar free	O	O	O	plastic pot
Yogurt, black cherry, raw sugar	O	H	O	plastic pot
Yogurt, black cherry, sugar free	O	O	O	plastic pot
Yogurt, blackcurrant, raw sugar	O	H	O	plastic pot
Yogurt, forest fruits, sugar free	O	O	O	plastic pot
Yogurt, mandarin, raw sugar	O	H	O	plastic pot
Yogurt, peach melba, raw sugar	O	H	O	plastic pot
Yogurt, pineapple, raw sugar	O	H	O	plastic pot
Yogurt, pineapple, sugar free	O	O	O	plastic pot
Yogurt, raspberry, raw sugar	O	H	O	plastic pot
Yogurt, raspberry, sugar free	O	O	O	plastic pot
Yogurt, strawberry, raw sugar	O	H	O	plastic pot
Yogurt, strawberry, sugar free	O	O	O	plastic pot

NOTES

NOTES

MARKS AND SPENCER PLC

St Michael®

Current trends suggest that consumers are increasingly seeking foods that they perceive to be 'Healthier'. This new awareness includes a questioning of the use of food additives. This provides further encouragement to our on-going development of products and distribution systems which help control safety and quality without over-reliance on permitted additives.

Marks & Spencer's policy has always been to develop and use whole natural fresh foods and ingredients, free wherever possible from 'Additives'. The use of food additives in St Michael foods has been closely monitored and controlled for many years. They are used only in those products where there is a proven need on grounds of safety, wholesomeness and aesthetic appeal.

We are now adopting an even more vigorous examination of our use of additives and are reviewing each of our products to see where further elimination of additives can be made. We are presently removing colouring from our range of bread-crumbed fish products. In dairy products, we have replaced with natural ingredients all artificial colourings and flavourings in our extensive range of low fat yogurts and, at the same time, have totally removed preservatives. These developments will continue with other food products.

There are some areas where additives are essential for product safety, for example, sodium nitrite in bacon and ham. In such instances, we will not hesitate to use the appropriate additives and will concentrate our energies on controlling the level of addition to check against unnecessary usage.

The additives used are selected from within the ranges approved by Government. Careful note is taken of investigative reports, both in this country and elsewhere, before agreement is given to use additives even though they feature in MAFF permitted lists.

Because of the rapid turnover in the product lines that Marks and Spencer sell, they have not submitted individual products for this edition of the *E for Additives Supermarket Shopping Guide.*

PRESTO

The policy of Argyll Foods, parent company of Presto stores, is to avoid where possible the use of additives, both in the branded goods it purchases and in its own-label goods. To this end we are seeking from suppliers a list of additives together with a justification for each one as the basis for joint discussions. Where additives are found to contribute nothing and where their removal does not make the product unacceptable to the customer, they will be removed.

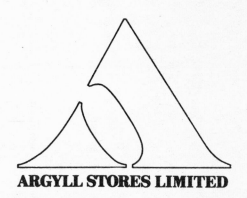

ARGYLL STORES LIMITED

PRESTO	Salt	Sugar	Flavour	Packaging
Almonds, blanched	0	0	0	film wrap
Almonds, flaked	0	0	0	film wrap
Almonds, ground	0	0	0	film wrap
Almonds, hickory flavour	H	0	F	film wrap
Almonds, whole	0	0	0	film wrap
Apple juice, pure	0	0	0	tetrapak
Apple, peach & nut salad	L	L	0	tub
Barley, pearl	0	0	0	film wrap
Bay leaves	0	0	0	plastic drum
Beans in tomato sauce	L	H	F	can
Beans, butter	0	0	0	film wrap
Beans, red kidney, in water	L	H	0	can
Beans, sliced green	0	0	0	frozen
Beans, whole green	0	0	0	frozen
Beef suet, shredded	0	0	0	carton
Beetroot, crinkle cut in vinegar	L	L	0	glass jar
Beetroot, sliced in vinegar	L	L	0	glass jar
Beetroot, whole in vinegar	L	L	0	glass jar
Biscuits, all butter	L	H	0	film wrap
Biscuits, digestive sweetmeal	L	H	0	film wrap
Biscuits, malted milk	L	H	F	film wrap

PRESTO	Salt	Sugar	Flavour	Packaging
Bouquet garni	0	0	0	plastic drum
Bourbon creams	L	H	F	film wrap
Bread baps, wholemeal	H	L	0	waxed paper wrap
Bread, wholemeal	H	L	0	waxed paper wrap
Brussels sprouts, selected	0	0	0	frozen
Butter, creamery	H	0	0	parchment wrap
Carrots, sliced, in salted water	L	0	0	can
Carrots, whole, in salted water	L	0	0	can
Carrots, young baby	0	0	0	frozen
Cauliflower florets	0	0	0	frozen
Cereals & pulses, mixed	0	0	0	film wrap
Cheese spread	L	0	0	rounds & tubs
Cheese, Caerphilly	H	0	0	vacuum pack
Cheese, Cheshire, coloured	H	0	0	vacuum pack
Cheese, Cheshire, natural	H	0	0	vacuum pack
Cheese, cottage, natural	L	0	0	tub
Cheese, cottage, with cheddar & onion	H	0	0	tub
Cheese, cottage, with chives	L	0	0	tub
Cheese, cottage, with pineapple	H	0	0	tub
Cheese, Derby	H	0	0	vacuum pack
Cheese, double Gloucester	H	0	0	vacuum pack

PRESTO	Salt	Sugar	Flavour	Packaging
Cheese, HP Cheddar, coloured	H	0	0	vacuum pack
Cheese, HP Cheddar, natural	H	0	0	vacuum pack
Cheese, HP matured Cheddar, coloured	H	0	0	vacuum pack
Cheese, HP matured Cheddar, natural	H	0	0	vacuum pack
Cheese, Irish Cheddar	H	0	0	vacuum pack
Cheese, Lancashire	H	0	0	vacuum pack
Cheese, red Leicester	H	0	0	vacuum pack
Cheese, Scottish Cheddar, coloured	H	0	0	vacuum pack
Cheese, Scottish Cheddar, natural	H	0	0	vacuum pack
Cheese, Wensleydale	H	0	0	vacuum pack
Chicken & mushroom pie	L	0	F	film wrap
Chicken roll, breast of	H	0	0	vacuum pack
Chips, chunky (Basics)	0	0	0	frozen
Chips, golden oven	0	0	0	frozen
Chocolate chip cookies	L	H	F	film wrap
Cinnamon, ground	0	0	0	plastic drum
Coconut, desiccated	0	0	0	film wrap
Cod fillets, prime	0	0	0	frozen
Coffee & chicory powder, instant	0	0	0	glass jar
Coffee granules, instant	0	0	0	glass jar
Coffee powder, instant	0	0	0	glass jar

PRESTO	Salt	Sugar	Flavour	Packaging
Coffee powder, instant (Basics)	0	0	0	carton
Coffee powder, instant, Brazilian Blend	0	0	0	glass jar
Coffee, ground, Continental Blend	0	0	0	carton
Coffee, ground, Original Blend	0	0	0	carton
Coffee, ground, Original Blend filter fine	0	0	0	carton
Coffee, ground, Special Blend	0	0	0	carton
Coffee, instant, Contintental Roast freeze dried	0	0	0	glass jar
Coffee, instant, Gold Roast freeze dried	0	L	0	glass jar
Coleslaw with mayonnaise	L	0	0	tub
Coley fillets, prime	0	H	0	frozen
Corn flakes	H	0	0	carton
Cornflour	0	H	0	carton
Cornish pasty	H	0	0	film wrap
Cream crackers	L	0	0	film wrap
Cream, fresh double, pasteurised	0	0	0	tub
Cream, fresh single, pasteurised	0	0	0	tub
Cream, fresh soured	0	0	0	tub
Cream, fresh spooning, pasteurised	0	0	0	tub
Cream, fresh whipping, pasteurised	0	L	0	tub
Crunchy whole wheat flakes (Basics)	L	0	0	film wrap
Currants, ready washed	0	0	0	film wrap

87

PRESTO	Salt	Sugar	Flavour	Packaging
Curry powder	H	O	O	plastic drum
Custard creams	L	H	F	film wrap
Custard creams (Basics)	L	H	F	film wrap
Devon toffees (Basics)	L	H	F	film wrap
Drinking chocolate	L	H	F	can
Drinking chocolate (Basics)	L	H	F	carton
Dutch crisbakes, original	L	H	O	waxed paper wrap
Dutch crisbakes, wholewheat	L	H	O	waxed paper wrap
Flour, plain	O	O	O	paper bag
Flour, self-raising	O	O	O	paper bag
Fruit shortcake	L	H	O	film wrap
Garibaldi biscuits	L	H	O	film wrap
Ginger nuts (Basics)	L	H	F	film wrap
Ginger, ground	O	O	O	plastic drum
Grapefruit juice, pure	O	O	O	tetrapak
Haddock fillets, prime	O	O	O	frozen
Haddock fillets, skinless	O	O	O	frozen
Hazelnuts	O	O	O	film wrap
Herbs, mixed, dried	O	O	O	plastic drum
High fibre bran cereal	H	H	O	carton
Honey, clear	O	O	O	glass jar

PRESTO	Salt	Sugar	Flavour	Packaging
Honey, set	O	O	O	glass jar
Hot oats cereal	O	O	O	carton
Jaffa cakes	O	H	F	film wrap
Lentils, split	O	O	O	film wrap
Macaroni, finest cut	O	O	O	film wrap
Macaroni, finest cut (Basics)	O	O	O	film wrap
Mandarin orange segments, in light syrup	O	H	O	can
Margarine	H	O	F	parchment wrap
Margarine, soft	H	O	F	tub
Margarine, soft (Basics)	H	O	F	tub
Margarine, sunflower	H	O	F	tub
Mayonnaise	L	O	F	glass jar
Milk chocolate digestive bars, 5	L	H	O	film wrap
Milk chocolate shortcake bars, 5	L	H	F	film wrap
Milk chocolate wafer fingers	L	H	F	film wrap
Milk, evaporated	O	O	O	can
Milk, skimmed dried with veg fat, 5 Quick Pints	O	H	O	plastic bottle
Milk, skimmed instant, low fat, spray-dried	O	O	O	can
Mint, dried	O	O	O	plastic drum
Mixed spice, ground	O	O	O	plastic drum
Muesli (Basics)	L	H	O	film wrap

PRESTO	Salt	Sugar	Flavour	Packaging
Mushrooms, sliced in salted water	L	0	0	can
Mushrooms, whole in salted water	L	0	0	can
Nice biscuits	L	H	F	film wrap
Nutmeg, ground	0	0	0	plastic drum
Nuts & fruit, mixed	0	0	0	film wrap
Nuts & fruit, mixed coated in dried vanilla flavour yogurt	0	H	F	film wrap
Nuts, Brazil	0	0	0	film wrap
Nuts, chopped mixed	0	0	0	film wrap
Oil, blended vegetable	0	0	0	plastic bottle
Oil, blended vegetable (Basics)	0	0	0	plastic bottle
Oil, pure corn	0	0	0	plastic bottle
Oil, pure olive	0	0	0	plastic bottle
Oil, pure solid vegetable	0	0	0	parchment wrap
Oil, pure soya	0	0	0	plastic bottle
Oil, pure sunflower	0	0	0	plastic bottle
Orange creams	L	H	F	film wrap
Orange juice, pure	0	0	0	tetrapak
Oregano, dried	0	0	0	plastic drum
Paprika, ground	0	0	0	plastic drum
Parsley, dried	0	0	0	plastic drum

PRESTO	Salt	Sugar	Flavour	Packaging
Peach halves in syrup	O	H	O	can
Peaches sliced in syrup	O	H	O	can
Peanut butter, crunchy	H	L	O	glass jar
Peanut butter, smooth	H	L	O	glass jar
Peanut kernels	O	O	O	film wrap
Peanuts & Raisins	O	O	F	film wrap
Peanuts, dry roasted	H	O	O	film wrap
Peanuts, salted	H	O	O	film wrap
Pear halves in syrup	O	H	O	can
Peas, dried marrowfat	O	O	O	film wrap
Peas, garden	O	O	O	frozen
Peas, garden (Basics)	O	O	O	frozen
Peas, yellow split	O	O	O	film wrap
Pepper, black ground	O	O	O	plastic drum
Pepper, black whole	O	O	O	plastic drum
Pepper, white ground	O	O	O	plastic drum
Pineapple juice, pure	O	O	O	tetrapak
Pizza with cheese & tomato	L	L	O	frozen
Pizza with ham & mushroom	L	L	O	frozen
Pizza, tomato & cheese (Basics)	L	L	O	frozen
Plaice fillets, prime	O	O	O	frozen

PRESTO	Salt	Sugar	Flavour	Packaging
Pork roast, prime	L	O	O	frozen
Potatoes, new, in salted water	H	O	F	can
Prawns, cooked, peeled	H	O	O	frozen
Prunes in syrup	O	H	O	can
Quick porridge oats	O	O	O	carton
Quick porridge oats (Basics)	O	O	O	film wrap
Raisins, seedless, ready washed	O	O	O	film wrap
Rice crunchies	H	H	O	carton
Rice, easy cook	O	O	O	film wrap
Rice, long grain	O	O	O	film wrap
Rice, long grain (Basics)	O	O	O	film wrap
Rice, round grain	O	O	O	film wrap
Rich shorties	L	H	F	film wrap
Rich tea fingers	L	H	F	film wrap
Rich tea fingers (Basics)	L	H	O	film wrap
Rosemary, dried	O	O	O	plastic drum
Sage, dried	O	O	O	plastic drum
Salad, cheese & pineapple	L	L	O	tub
Salad, curried vegetable	L	L	O	tub
Salad, mixed vegetable	L	L	O	tub
Salad, potato with chives	L	L	O	tub

PRESTO	Salt	Sugar	Flavour	Packaging
Salt, pure cooking	H	O	O	film wrap
Salt, table, free flowing	H	O	O	plastic drum
Shortbread, all butter assortment	L	H	O	film wrap
Shortbread, all butter fingers	L	H	O	film wrap
Shortbread, all butter, petticoat tails	L	H	O	film wrap
Shortcake	L	H	O	film wrap
Shortcake (Basics)	L	O	O	film wrap
Spaghetti	O	O	O	film wrap
Spaghetti (Basics)	O	O	F	carton
Stuffing mix, parsley & thyme	H	L	O	carton
Stuffing mix, sage & onion	H	L	O	film wrap
Sugar, Demerara, natural raw cane	O	H	O	can
Sweetcorn with red peppers in water	L	L	O	frozen
Sweetcorn, sun ripe	O	O	O	can
Sweetcorn, whole kernel in water	L	L	O	carton
Swiss style breakfast cereal	L	H	O	glass jar
Tartare sauce	H	H	F	carton
Tea	O	O	O	carton
Tea-bags	O	O	O	carton
Tea-bags (Basics)	O	O	O	carton
Thyme, dried	O	O	O	plastic drum

PRESTO	Salt	Sugar	Flavour	Packaging
Tomatoes, peeled plum, in tomato juice	0	0	0	can
Tropical fruit drink	0	H	F	tetrapak
Vegetables, mixed	0	0	0	frozen
Vegetables, mixed, casserole	0	0	0	frozen
Vegetables, mixed, in salted water	L	0	0	can
Vegetables, special, mixed	0	0	0	frozen
Vinegar, distilled malt	0	0	0	glass bottle
Walnuts	0	0	0	film wrap
Water, mineral, sparkling natural	0	0	0	glass bottle
Water, soda	0	0	0	glass bottle
Whiting fillets, skinless	L	L	0	frozen
Whole wheat cereal, breakfast bisk	0	H	0	carton
Yogurt, black cherry, low fat	0	H	F	tub
Yogurt, fruits of the forest, low fat	0	H	F	tub
Yogurt, hazelnut, low fat	0	H	0	tub
Yogurt, natural low fat	0	0	0	tub

NOTES

NOTES

SAFEWAY

SAFEWAY	Salt	Sugar	Flavour	Packaging
Almonds, ground	O	O	O	box
Almonds, sugared	O	H	O	
Almonds, whole	O	O	O	delicatessen
Alutikian	H	O	O	carton
Apple juice, fresh English	O	O	O	
Apple juice, long life English	O	O	O	
Apple juice, pure	O	O	O	
Apple juice, sparkling	O	O	O	bottle
Barley, pearl	O	O	O	
Bay leaves	H	L	O	
Beans, baked	O	O	O	can
Beans, broad	O	O	O	frozen
Beans, butter	O	O	O	dried
Beans, cut green	O	O	O	frozen
Beans, haricot	O	O	O	dried
Beans, red kidney	H	H	O	can
Beans, sliced green	H	O	O	can
Beans, sliced green	O	O	O	frozen
Beans, whole green	H	O	O	can
Beans, whole green	O	O	O	frozen
Beef spread	H	O	O	delicatessen

SAFEWAY	Salt	Sugar	Flavour	Packaging
Beef, topside, cooked	H	L	O	vacuum packed
Beef, topside, cooked	H	L	O	delicatessen
Beefburger	H	L	F	frozen
Beefburger, quarter-pounder	H	L	F	frozen
Beefy drink	H	O	X	jar
Bouquet Garni	O	O	O	
Brazil nuts, milk chocolate	O	H	F	box
Brazil nuts, plain chocolate	O	H	F	box
Broccoli spears	O	O	O	frozen
Brussels sprouts	O	O	O	frozen
Burger, economy	H	L	F	frozen
Butter, Cornish	H	O	O	
Butter, Devon roll	H	O	O	
Butter, English, garlic	H	O	O	
Butter, English salted, sweet cream	H	O	O	
Butter, Scandinavian style slightly salted	H	O	O	
Butter, Scandinavian style unsalted	O	O	O	
Butter, Welsh, herb & garlic	H	O	O	
Cabbage, fresh shredded	O	O	O	tray
Caraway seeds	O	O	O	
Carrots, baby	O	O	O	frozen

SAFEWAY	Salt	Sugar	Flavour	Packaging
Carrots, sliced	H	O	O	can
Carrots, sliced, with no added salt	O	O	O	can
Carrots, whole	H	O	O	can
Carrots, whole, with no added salt	O	O	O	can
Cauliflower	L	O	O	frozen
Cauliflower cheese	O	O	O	chilled
Cayenne pepper	X	O	O	
Cheese, Bel Paese	X	O	O	delicatessen
Cheese, Belle Normande	H	O	O	delicatessen
Cheese, blue Cheshire	H	O	O	
Cheese, blue Stilton	H	O	O	
Cheese, blue Wensleydale	H	O	O	
Cheese, blue, full fat soft	H	O	O	
Cheese, Brie	H	O	O	
Cheese, Caerphilly	H	O	O	
Cheese, Camembert	H	O	O	
Cheese, Cheddar	H	O	O	
Cheese, Cheshire	H	O	O	
Cheese, cooking	H	O	O	
Cheese, cottage	H	O	O	
Cheese, cottage, with Cheddar & onion	H	O	O	

SAFEWAY	Salt	Sugar	Flavour	Packaging
Cheese, cottage, with chives	H	0	0	
Cheese, cottage, with date & walnut	H	0	0	
Cheese, cottage, with onion & peppers	H	0	0	
Cheese, cottage, with pineapple	H	0	0	
Cheese, cottage, with prawns	H	0	0	
Cheese, cottage, with salmon & cucumber	H	0	0	
Cheese, curd, medium fat	H	0	0	
Cheese, Derby	H	0	0	
Cheese, double Gloucester	H	0	0	
Cheese, Esrom, medium fat soft	H	0	0	
Cheese, Gloucester	X	0	0	delicatessen
Cheese, goat milk	L	0	0	delicatessen
Cheese, herb Roulé	H	0	0	
Cheese, Huntsman	H	0	0	
Cheese, Ilchester Cheddar	X	0	0	delicatessen
Cheese, Jarlesberg	H	0	0	
Cheese, Lancashire	H	0	0	
Cheese, Lymeswold	X	0	0	delicatessen
Cheese, Maasdam	H	0	0	delicatessen
Cheese, Melbury	H	0	0	delicatessen
Cheese, mini Cheddar & herbs	H	0	0	delicatessen

SAFEWAY	Salt	Sugar	Flavour	Packaging
Cheese, mini Cheddar & mustard	H	0	0	delicatessen
Cheese, mini double Gloucester & chives	H	0	0	delicatessen
Cheese, mini sage Derby	H	0	0	delicatessen
Cheese, mountain Gorgonzola	H	0	0	
Cheese, Mozzarella	L	0	0	delicatessen
Cheese, Mycella	X	0	0	
Cheese, Parmesan	H	0	0	
Cheese, Pipo Crème	X	0	0	
Cheese, Port Salut	H	0	0	
Cheese, Pyrenean	X	0	0	delicatessen
Cheese, processed Cheddar slices	H	0	0	delicatessen
Cheese, processed slices	H	0	0	delicatessen
Cheese, Rambol walnut	X	0	0	delicatessen
Cheese, red Cheshire	H	0	0	
Cheese, red Leicester	H	0	0	
Cheese, Ricotta	L	0	0	
Cheese, Roquefort	H	0	0	
Cheese, sage Derby	H	0	0	
Cheese, soft, full fat	H	0	0	
Cheese, soft, full fat, with chives	H	0	0	
Cheese, soft, full fat, with herbs & garlic	X	0	0	delicatessen

SAFEWAY	Salt	Sugar	Flavour	Packaging
Cheese, soft, full fat, with pepper	X	O	O	delicatessen
Cheese, soft, low fat	L	O	O	
Cheese, soft, skimmed milk	O	O	O	delicatessen
Cheese, Somerset Brie	L	O	O	
Cheese, superb creamery	H	O	O	
Cheese, Tilsit	H	O	O	
Cheese, traditional Normandy Drakkar	X	O	O	delicatessen
Cheese, Vieux Pane	X	O	O	
Cheese, Wensleydale	H	O	O	
Cheese, white Stilton	H	O	O	
Chicken breasts, en croûte	L	O	F	fresh
Chicken Cordon Bleu	L	O	O	fresh
Chicken Kiev	O	O	O	fresh
Chicken livers, home produced	O	O	O	fresh
Chicken Maryland	L	O	O	fresh
Chilli Con Carne	O	O	O	chilled
Chips, oven	O	O	O	frozen
Chips, potato	O	O	O	frozen
Chives	O	O	O	
Chocolate baubles	O	H	O	box
Chocolate buttons, milk	O	H	O	packet

SAFEWAY	Salt	Sugar	Flavour	Packaging
Chocolate Father Christmas	O	H	O	box
Chocolate hazelnut spread	L	H	F	
Chocolate mini coins	O	H	F	box
Chocolate mini eggs	O	H	X	box
Cinnamon	O	O	O	
Cloves	O	O	O	
Cocoa	O	O	F	
Coconut, desiccated	O	O	O	
Cod fillets	L	O	O	frozen
Cod, in batter	L	O	O	frozen
Cod, in breadcrumbs	H	O	O	frozen
Cod's roe, fresh smoked	O	O	O	delicatessen
Coffee beans	O	O	O	
Coffee granules, instant	O	O	O	
Coffee powder	O	O	O	
Coffee, filter, all types	O	O	O	
Coffee, freeze dried (Choice)	O	O	O	
Coffee, freeze dried, decaffeinated	O	O	O	
Coffee, Gold	O	O	O	
Coffee, ground, all types	O	O	O	
Coffee, with chicory	O	O	O	

SAFEWAY	Salt	Sugar	Flavour	Packaging
Coleslaw	L	L	O	tub
Coleslaw, low calorie	L	L	O	delicatessen
Coleslaw, low calorie	L	L	O	tub
Coleslaw, prawn	L	L	O	delicatessen
Conserve, apricot	O	H	O	
Conserve, black cherry, Swiss	O	H	O	
Conserve, blackcurrant	O	H	O	
Conserve, morello cherry	O	H	O	
Conserve, raspberry	O	H	O	
Conserve, strawberry	O	H	O	
Corn on the cob	O	O	O	frozen
Corn, mini	O	O	O	frozen
Cornflakes	H	H	O	
Cornflour	O	O	O	
Cornish wafer	H	O	O	biscs for cheese box
Courgettes	O	O	O	frozen
Courgettes, stir fry	O	O	O	tray
Cream crackers	H	O	O	assorted biscs pack
Cream, double	O	O	O	

SAFEWAY	Salt	Sugar	Flavour	Packaging
Cream, extra thick	O	O	O	
Cream, half	O	O	O	
Cream, single	O	O	O	
Cream, soured	O	O	O	
Cream, sterilised	O	O	O	can
Cream, whipping	O	O	O	
Crisps, ready salted	H	O	O	
Crunchy cereal	L	H	O	
Currants	O	O	O	
Curry powder	O	O	O	
Curry powder, Madras	O	O	O	
Custard creams	L	H	F	assorted biscs pack
Custard creams	L	H	F	assorted creams pack
Dolmades	H	O	O	delicatessen
Dressing, French oil	H	O	O	
Dressing, garlic oil	H	O	O	
Dressing, Italian oil	H	O	O	
Dressing, mustard oil	H	O	O	
Drinking chocolate	O	L	F	

SAFEWAY	Salt	Sugar	Flavour	Packaging
Eel, shoestring fillets	H	O	O	delicatessen
Eel, whole, smoked	H	O	O	delicatessen
Eleven plus	O	L	O	
Fibre bran	H	H	O	
Finger creams	L	H	F	assorted creams pack
Fish fingers	L	O	O	frozen
Fish fingers, prime cod	L	O	O	frozen
Flour, plain	O	O	O	
Flour, self raising	O	O	O	
Flour, wholewheat, strong plain	O	O	O	
Fruit cake, all butter wheatmeal	L	H	O	clear plastic wrap
Gherkins, midget	H	L	L	delicatessen
Ginger creams	L	H	F	
Ginger, ground	O	O	O	
Grape juice, red sparkling	O	O	O	bottle
Grape juice, red, long life	O	O	O	
Grape juice, white sparkling	O	O	O	bottle
Grape juice, white, long life	O	O	O	
Grapefruit juice, pure	O	O	O	
Grapefruit juice, Texan ruby red	O	O	O	carton

SAFEWAY	Salt	Sugar	Flavour	Packaging
Haddock fillets	O	O	O	frozen
Haddock in batter	L	O	O	frozen
Haddock in breadcrumbs	L	O	O	frozen
Halva	O	H	O	delicatessen
Halva, almond	O	H	O	delicatessen
Halva, chocolate	O	H	F	delicatessen
Halva, peanut	O	H	F	delicatessen
Halva, pistachio	O	H	F	delicatessen
Halva, vanilla	O	H	F	delicatessen
Halva, vanilla with honey	O	H	F	delicatessen
Hawaiian drink	O	L	O	carton
Herbs, mixed	O	O	O	
Herrings, loose pickling	H	O	O	delicatessen
Herrings, matjes	H	O	O	delicatessen
Herrings, roll mop	H	H	O	delicatessen
Honey, Canadian	O	O	O	
Honey, clear	O	O	O	
Honey, Mexican	O	O	O	
Honey, set	O	O	O	
Hot oat cereal	O	O	O	
Houmous	H	O	O	delicatessen

SAFEWAY	Salt	Sugar	Flavour	Packaging
Jam, apricot, no added sugar	O	O	O	
Jam, blackcurrant, no added sugar	O	O	O	
Jam, raspberry, no added sugar	O	O	O	
Jam, strawberry, no added sugar	O	O	O	
Kebabs, beef	O	O	O	chilled
Kebabs, lamb	O	O	O	chilled
Kebabs, pork	L	O	O	chilled
Keftedes	L	O	O	delicatessen
Kouskous	L	O	O	delicatessen
Lasagne, egg	L	O	O	
Lasagne, verdi, egg	O	O	O	
Lentils, dried split	H	O	O	
Loaves, stoneground wholemeal sliced	O	O	O	pre-packed
Macaroni	O	L	O	
Malibu mix	L	H	O	
Malted food drink	O	O	O	
Mandarins, Spanish, in light syrup	L	O	O	can
Margarine, cooking	H	O	O	
Margarine, deluxe	H	O	O	
Margarine, soya	L	O	O	
Margarine, sunflower	H	O	O	

SAFEWAY	Salt	Sugar	Flavour	Packaging
Margarine, sunflower, salt free	O	O	O	
Margarine, table	H	O	O	
Marjoram	O	O	O	
Marmalade, no added sugar	O	O	O	
Mayonnaise	L	L	O	
Mayonnaise, American style	L	L	O	
Mayonnaise, garlic	L	L	O	
Mayonnaise, lemon	L	L	O	
Mayonnaise, mild curry	L	L	O	
Mayonnaise, mustard	L	L	O	
Meringue nests	O	H	O	
Mexicana mix	O	O	O	box
Milk chocolate biscuits, half covered	L	H	F	assorted biscs pack
Milk, dried Fast Pints	O	O	O	
Milk, evaporated	O	O	O	can
Milk, fresh pasteurised	O	O	O	
Milk, instant dried	O	O	O	
Milk, soya	L	L	O	
Milk, sterilised	O	O	O	bottle
Milk, UHT	O	O	O	carton

SAFEWAY	Salt	Sugar	Flavour	Packaging
Mint, dried	O	O	O	
Moussaka	L	O	O	chilled
Muffins, wholemeal	H	L	O	plastic bag
Mushroom à la grecque	H	O	O	delicatessen
Mushrooms, sliced	H	O	O	can
Mushrooms, stir fry	O	O	O	tray
Mushrooms, whole button	H	O	O	can
Nutmeg, ground	O	O	O	
Nutmeg, whole	O	O	O	
Nuts & fruit, mixed	O	O	O	
Nuts, mixed roasted salted	H	O	O	
Oil, corn	O	O	O	
Oil, olive	O	O	O	
Oil, olive, extra virgin	O	O	O	
Oil, soya	O	O	O	
Oil, sunflower	O	O	O	
Oil, vegetable	O	O	O	
Olives, black, all varieties	H	O	O	delicatessen
Olives, green, all varieties	H	O	O	delicatessen
Olives, stuffed	H	O	O	delicatessen
Onion Bhajia	L	O	O	delicatessen

SAFEWAY	Salt	Sugar	Flavour	Packaging
Onions, sliced	O	O	O	frozen
Orange & apricot drink	O	H	O	carton
Orange & apricot drink, long life	O	H	O	
Orange C	O	H	O	carton, chilled
Orange juice	O	O	O	carton, long life
Orange juice, pure	O	O	O	
Oregano	O	O	O	
Paprika	O	O	O	
Parsley	O	O	O	
Pasta bows	O	O	O	
Pasta quills	O	O	O	
Pasta shells	O	O	O	
Pasta twists	O	O	O	
Paste, crab	H	O	F	jar
Paste, salmon	H	O	O	delicatessen
Paste, salmon & shrimp	H	O	O	jar
Pâté, salmon	L	O	F	delicatessen
Peach halves in fruit juice	O	O	O	can
Peach halves in syrup	O	H	O	can
Peach slices in fruit juice	O	O	O	can
Peach slices in syrup	O	H	O	can

SAFEWAY	Salt	Sugar	Flavour	Packaging
Peaches & pears in syrup	O	H	O	can
Peanut butter, crunchy	L	O	O	
Peanut butter, smooth	L	O	O	
Peanuts, blanched & raisins	O	O	O	
Peanuts, raisins & chocolate chips	O	O	O	
Peanuts, roasted salted	H	O	O	
Peanuts, shelled	O	O	O	
Pear halves in natural juice	O	H	O	can
Pear halves in syrup	O	O	O	can
Pear quarters in natural juice	O	H	O	can
Pear quarters in syrup	O	O	O	can
Peas	O	O	O	frozen
Peas, dried	O	O	O	
Peas, dried split	L	L	O	
Peas, minted	O	O	F	frozen
Pepper, black	O	O	O	
Pepper, white	O	O	O	
Peppercorns, black	O	O	O	
Peppercorns, white	O	O	O	
Peppers, mixed	O	O	O	frozen
Petit pois	L	L	O	can

SAFEWAY	Salt	Sugar	Flavour	Packaging
Petit pois	O	O	O	frozen
Petticoat Tails	L	H	O	
Pineapple juice	O	O	O	carton, chilled
Pineapple juice, pure	O	O	O	carton, longlife
Pineapple pieces in natural juice	O	O	O	can
Pineapple rings in natural juice	O	O	O	can
Pineapple, crushed, in natural juice	O	L	O	can
Pizza bread, wholemeal, 7 & 10 inch	L	L	O	
Pizza, vegetable, wholemeal	L	O	O	
Plaice fillets	O	L	O	frozen
Pork, leg, cooked	H	L	O	vacuum packed
Pork, leg, cooked	H	L	O	delicatessen
Porridge oats	O	O	O	
Potatoes, Jersey Royal	H	O	F	can
Potatoes, new, small	O	O	F	can
Prunes, dried	O	O	O	
Quiche, Espagne	O	O	O	box
Quick cooking oats	O	O	O	
Raisins	O	O	O	
Ratatouille	L	L	O	can
Ratatouille	O	O	O	frozen

SAFEWAY	Salt	Sugar	Flavour	Packaging
Ratatouille, fresh vegetables	O	O	O	tray
Ravioli	H	L	O	can
Rice crunchies	H	H	O	
Rice, basmati	O	O	O	
Rice, brown	O	O	O	
Rice, easy cook	O	O	O	
Rice, flaked	O	O	O	
Rice, ground	O	O	O	
Rice, long grain	O	O	O	
Rice, pudding	O	H	O	dried
Rice pudding, creamed	O	H	O	can
Rice, traditional creamed	H	L	O	can
Rolls, snack wholemeal	O	O	O	plastic bag
Sage	O	O	O	
Salad, Acapulco	L	L	O	delicatessen
Salad, apple & coleslaw	O	O	O	delicatessen
Salad, apple & peach	L	L	O	delicatessen
Salad, apple & sultana	L	L	O	tub
Salad, bean, mixed	L	L	O	can
Salad, beetroot & orange	O	O	O	delicatessen
Salad, carrot & nut, crunchy	O	O	O	tub

SAFEWAY	Salt	Sugar	Flavour	Packaging
Salad, celery & chicken	O	O	O	delicatessen
Salad, cheese, pineapple & wholemeal pasta	O	O	O	tub
Salad, chicken in sweet & sour sauce	L	H	O	delicatessen
Salad, Chinese beansprout	L	O	O	delicatessen
Salad, Chinese leaf and sweetcorn	O	O	O	tray
Salad, coleslaw	L	L	O	delicatessen
Salad, corn	O	O	O	delicatessen
Salad, cucumber & orange in yoghurt dressing	L	O	O	delicatessen
Salad, egg, potato & onion	L	O	O	delicatessen
Salad, Florida	O	O	O	delicatesen
Salad, leek	O	O	O	delicatessen
Salad, Madras rice	L	L	O	delicatessen
Salad, mixed vegetables in French dressing	L	O	O	delicatessen
Salad, mixed, with beansprouts	O	L	O	tray
Salad, potato	L	L	O	tub
Salad, potato, coarse cut	L	L	O	delicatessen
Salad, potato, new	L	O	O	delicatessen
Salad, potato, spicy	L	L	O	tub
Salad, red kidney bean	O	O	O	delicatessen
Salad, rice	L	O	O	tub
Salad, rice & vegetable	O	O	O	delicatessen

SAFEWAY	Salt	Sugar	Flavour	Packaging
Salad, Russian	L	L	O	delicatessen
Salad, Spanish	L	L	O	delicatessen
Salad, Spanish	L	L	O	tub
Salad, vegetable	L	L	O	tub
Salad, walnut & apple	O	O	O	tray
Salmon, grilse, smoked	H	O	O	delicatessen
Salmon, smoked	H	O	O	delicatessen
Salmon, smoked, sliced	H	O	O	delicatessen
Salmon, smoked, sliced, imported	H	O	O	delicatessen
Salt, cooking	H	O	O	
Salt, table	H	O	O	
Samosa, meat	H	O	O	delicatessen
Samosa, vegetable	H	O	O	delicatessen
Sardines in oil	H	O	O	can
Sardines in tomato sauce	H	O	O	can
Sauce, Bolognese	H	O	O	jar
Sauce, cranberry	O	L	O	jar
Sauce, tartare, yoghurt	H	H	O	chilled
Savoury spread	H	L	F	
Savoury twigs	H	O	O	
Scottish oatcakes	H	O	O	assorted biscs pack

SAFEWAY	Salt	Sugar	Flavour	Packaging
Semolina, dried	O	O	O	
Sesame crackers	H	O	F	
Shortbread fingers	L	H	O	
Soup, cream of tomato	L	L	O	can
Spaghetti, long	O	O	O	
Spaghetti, short	O	O	O	
Spinach, chopped	O	O	O	frozen
Spinach, creamed	L	O	O	frozen
Spinach, leaf	O	O	O	frozen
Spinach, mini portions	O	O	O	frozen
Spread, low fat	H	O	O	
Spring roll, Chinese style chicken	H	O	O	delicatessen
Spring roll, Chinese style vegetable	H	O	O	delicatessen
Stir fry, Oriental	O	O	O	frozen
Stir fry, risotto	O	O	O	frozen
Stir fry, Southern	O	O	O	frozen
Stuffing mix, parsley & thyme	H	O	O	packet
Stuffing mix, sage & onion	H	O	O	packet
Suet	O	O	O	
Sweetcorn	O	O	O	
Swiss style cereal	L	H	O	frozen

SAFEWAY	Salt	Sugar	Flavour	Packaging
Tahinasalata	H	O	O	delicatessen
Tapioca, seed pearl	O	O	O	
Tea bags	O	O	O	
Tea, Earl Gray	O	O	O	
Tea, premium	O	O	O	
Tea, special	O	O	O	
Thyme	O	O	O	
Tomato juice	L	H	O	carton
Tropical fruit drink	O	O	O	carton
Trout, fresh smoked	H	O	O	delicatessen
Tsatsiki	H	L	O	delicatessen
Turkey, cooked	H	L	O	vacuum packed
Turkey, cooked	H	O	O	delicatessen
Vegetable pattie	O	O	O	delicatessen
Vegetables, mixed	O	O	O	frozen
Vegetables, mixed casserole	H	O	O	frozen
Vegetables, mixed Continental	O	O	O	can
Vegetables, mixed farmhouse	O	O	O	frozen
Vegetables, mixed special	O	O	O	frozen
Vinegar, cider	O	O	O	
Vinegar, distilled	O	O	O	

SAFEWAY	Salt	Sugar	Flavour	Packaging
Vinegar, red wine	O	O	O	
Vinegar, white wine	O	O	O	
Wafers	L	H	F	assorted biscs pack
Wafers	L	H	F	assorted creams pack
Water, natural sparkling	O	O	O	
Water, natural still	O	O	O	
Water, soda	L	L	O	
Whole wheat biscuits	L	L	O	
Whole wheat flakes	O	H	O	
Yoghurt, apple	O	O	F	
Yoghurt, apple & rhubarb, fresh milk unsweetened	O	H	O	
Yoghurt, black cherry	O	H	F	
Yoghurt, black cherry, velvet	O	H	F	
Yoghurt, blackcurrant	O	H	F	
Yoghurt, blueberry	L	H	F	
Yoghurt, chocolate	O	H	F	
Yoghurt, coconut	O	H	F	
Yoghurt, elderberry & cherry	O	H	F	

SAFEWAY	Salt	Sugar	Flavour	Packaging
Yoghurt, exotic, French style	O	H	F	
Yoghurt, fruit of the forest	O	H	F	
Yoghurt, hazelnut	O	H	F	
Yoghurt, lemon, French style	O	H	F	
Yoghurt, lychee	O	H	F	
Yoghurt, mandarin	O	H	F	
Yoghurt, natural	O	O	O	
Yoghurt, natural set	O	O	O	
Yoghurt, orange, fresh milk unsweetened	O	O	O	
Yoghurt, passion fruit & melon	O	H	F	
Yoghurt, peach & papaya	O	H	F	
Yoghurt, peach melba, fresh milk unsweetened	O	O	O	
Yoghurt, peach, pineapple & passion fruit, fresh milk unsweetened	O	O	O	
Yoghurt, pear & raspberry	O	H	F	
Yoghurt, raspberry, fresh milk unsweetened	O	O	O	
Yoghurt, strawberry, French style	O	H	F	
Yoghurt, strawberry, fresh milk unsweetened	O	O	O	
Yoghurt, tropical	O	H	F	
Yoghurt, tropical fruit, velvet	O	H	F	
Yoghurt, vanilla, French style	O	H	F	

SAFEWAY	Salt	Sugar	Flavour	Packaging
Yogurt dressing, blue cheese	L	O	F	chilled
Yogurt dressing, herb & garlic	H	L	O	chilled
Yogurt dressing, thousand island	H	L	O	chilled

NOTES

NOTES

SAINSBURY'S

For some considerable time Sainsbury's has been conscious of an increasing awareness and concern among consumers on the subject of artificial additives. As a direct result of this we have categorized artificial additives under three headings:

1   Those considered to be entirely harmless.

2   Those artificial additives we should like to replace in the long term with natural counterparts if they are available.

3   Those additives, the majority of which are colourings, where there is some information suggesting a small section of the population may be adversely affected by them.

It is in the last category that our buyers and food technologists have concentrated during 1985. However, even earlier than this, we had begun work on the reduction of additives in several of our own-label lines including the removal of colouring in such lines as frozen pastry, lasagne and sausage rolls.

Currently we are taking action in three distinct ways:

1   Firstly, by ensuring that new own label products contain artificial additives *only* if they are absolutely essential, i.e. to prevent early deterioration of the product.

2   Secondly, by increasing the range of products that are free from artificial additives, e.g., canned vegetables free from

sugar, salt, or colour; white marzipan with no added colouring; a range of conserves free from added colours and preservatives. These are just a few examples of already well-established lines.

3 Thirdly, to review every existing own label product and establish which artificial additives can be removed or replaced with natural alternatives. Such examples can be seen in our 100 per cent natural French Recipe yogurts and Mr Men yogurts with no artificial additives; tartrazine (E102) has been removed from a wide range of products including ice-cream, soup-in-a-cup and fish fingers; brown FK has been removed from our smoked mackerel fillets.

Although considerable progress has now been made, with over 3,000 own label food and drink lines to consider, work is naturally still in progress. Indeed, this work has become an integral part of our overall quality control procedure and accordingly is approached with the same commitment with which Sainsbury's has built its good food reputation.

In addition, we should like to point out that all the added flavourings used in our yogurts are of natural origins.

SAINSBURY'S	Salt	Sugar	Flavour	Packaging
Almond flakes	O	O	O	poly bag
Almond flavour	O	O	O	miniature bottle
Almonds	O	O	O	poly bag
Almonds, blanched	O	O	O	poly bag
Almonds, ground	O	O	O	poly bag
Almonds, whole	O	O	O	poly bag
Alpine strawberry fromage dessert (Summer 1986)	X	X	X	
Anchovies, fillets, in pure olive oil	H	O	O	can
Apple & blackberry fruit filling	O	H	O	can
Apple juice, English	O	O	O	carton
Apple juice, pure	O	O	O	chilled, carton
Apple juice, pure	O	O	O	carton
Apple juice, pure English	O	O	O	chilled, carton
Apple strudel	L	H	O	frozen
Apple, slices	O	O	O	can
Apple, stewed	O	H	O	can
Apricot, halves, in fruit juice	O	O	O	can
Apricot, halves, in syrup	O	H	O	can
Bakewell tart	L	H	F	frozen
Baking powder	O	O	O	drum

SAINSBURY'S	Salt	Sugar	Flavour	Packaging
Baps, granary wholemeal	H	L	O	
Baps, Hovis stoneground wholemeal	H	L	O	
Baps, wholemeal	H	L	O	
Baps, wholemeal round	H	L	O	poly bag
Barley, pearl	O	O	O	
Batter mix	L	O	O	
Bean salad, mixed	L	L	O	can
Beans in tomato sauce	L	L	O	can
Beans in tomato sauce with pork sausages (Autumn 1986)	X	X	X	can
Beans, borlotti	L	L	O	can
Beans, broad	L	O	O	can
Beans, broad	O	O	O	frozen
Beans, broad, in water	O	O	O	can
Beans, butter	O	O	O	poly bag
Beans, chilli (from Autumn 1986)	X	X	X	can
Beans, curried	L	L	O	can
Beans, cut	O	O	O	frozen
Beans, green, cut	L	O	O	can
Beans, green, cut, in water	O	O	O	can
Beans, haricot	O	O	O	poly bag

SAINSBURY'S	Salt	Sugar	Flavour	Packaging
Beans, red kidney	H	L	O	can
Beans, red kidney	O	O	O	poly bag
Beans, red kidney in water	X	X	X	can
Beans, sliced	O	O	O	frozen
Beans, stringless, cut	L	O	O	cah
Beans, whole	O	O	O	frozen
Beef & onion spread	L	O	O	jar
Beef spread	H	O	O	delicatessen
Beef, potted	H	O	O	jar
Beef, topside, roast	X	X	O	pre-packed
Beetroot, baby, whole in sweet vinegar	L	H	O	jar
Beetroot, baby, whole pickled	O	L	O	jar
Beetroot, cooked	O	O	O	fresh
Beetroot, crinkle cut in sweet vinegar	L	H	O	jar
Beetroot, sliced in sweet vinegar	L	L	O	jar
Bicarbonate of soda	O	O	O	drum
Biscuits, all butter	L	H	O	
Biscuits, all butter crunch	L	H	F	
Biscuits, all butter fruit	L	H	O	
Biscuits, all butter shortbread fingers	L	H	O	
Biscuits, butter almond cookies	L	H	F	

SAINSBURY'S	Salt	Sugar	Flavour	Packaging
Biscuits, butter sandwich creams	L	H	O	
Biscuits, chocolate & nut cookies	L	H	O	
Biscuits, chocolate chip cookies	L	H	O	
Biscuits, chocolate chip oat & coconut crunch	L	H	F	
Biscuits, chocolate chip shortbread rings	L	H	O	
Biscuits, coconut cookies	L	H	F	
Biscuits, coconut creams	L	H	O	
Biscuits, coconut rings	L	H	O	
Biscuits, crunch creams	L	H	O	
Biscuits, custard creams	L	H	O	
Biscuits, digestives, milk chocolate (6)	L	H	O	
Biscuits, digestives, milk chocolate	L	H	O	
Biscuits, digestives, plain chocolate	L	H	O	
Biscuits, digestives, sweetmeal	L	H	O	
Biscuits, fig rolls	L	H	O	
Biscuits, fruit & nut, milk chocolate (6)	L	H	O	
Biscuits, fruit shortcake	L	H	O	
Biscuits, ginger creams	L	H	O	
Biscuits, Highland shortbread rounds	L	H	O	
Biscuits, lemon puffs	L	H	O	
Biscuits, milk chocolate crunch	L	H	O	

SAINSBURY'S	Salt	Sugar	Flavour	Packaging
Biscuits, milk chocolate fingers	L	H	F	
Biscuits, mini gingers	L	H	F	
Biscuits, mint wafer, milk chocolate (6)	L	H	O	
Biscuits, morning coffee	H	H	F	
Biscuits, oatmeal bran	L	H	O	
Biscuits, peanut crunch	L	H	O	
Biscuits, petticoat tails	L	H	O	
Biscuits, rich tea fingers	L	H	O	
Biscuits, sandwich creams	L	H	O	
Biscuits, shortcake	L	H	O	
Biscuits, shortcake, milk chocolate (6)	L	H	O	
Biscuits, shorties	L	H	O	
Biscuits, spicy fruit crunch	L	H	O	
Biscuits, sweetmeal creams	L	H	O	
Biscuits, Thistle shortbread	L	H	O	
Biscuits, tangy orange creams	L	H	F	
Biscuits, treacle crunch creams	L	H	O	
Biscuits, walnut shorties	L	H	O	
Biscuits, wholemeal shortbread fingers	L	H	O	
Biscuits, wholewheat honey sandwich	L	H	O	
Black Cherry double dessert (Summer 1986)	X	X	X	

SAINSBURY'S	Salt	Sugar	Flavour	Packaging
Blackberries, in fruit juice, unsweetened	O	O	O	can
Blackcurrant drink	X	X	X	carton
Blackcurrant fromage dessert (Summer 1986)	X	X	X	
Blackcurrants, in fruit juice, unsweetened	O	O	O	can
Bouquet garni	O	O	O	sachet
Bran flakes	H	H	O	carton
Brazil kernels	O	O	O	poly bag
Brazils, milk chocolate	O	H	O	
Brazils, plain chocolate	O	H	O	
Bread mix, granary	L	O	O	
Bread mix, white	L	O	O	
Bread, granary wholemeal	H	L	O	
Bread, Hovis stoneground wholemeal, uncut	H	L	O	
Bread, pitta, wholemeal	L	O	O	
Bread, soft wholemeal, fruited	H	H	O	
Bread, stoneground mini loaves	H	L	O	
Bread, stoneground wholemeal batch	H	L	O	
Bread, stoneground wholemeal, all types	H	L	O	
Bread, wholemeal batch with cracked wheat	H	L	O	
Bread, wholemeal batch with sesame seeds	H	L	O	
Bread, wholemeal soft batch	H	L	O	

SAINSBURY'S	Salt	Sugar	Flavour	Packaging
Bread, wholemeal, medium sliced	H	L	O	
Bread, wholemeal, uncut	H	L	O	
Breadcrumbs (Summer 1986)	X	X	X	carton/drum
Breakfast bran	H	H	O	carton
Broccoli spears	O	O	O	frozen
Bubble & squeak	H	O	O	frozen
Buns, mini wholemeal hot cross	L	H	F	
Buns, mini wholemeal, spiced fruit	L	H	F	
Buns, wholemeal hot cross	L	H	F	
Buns, wholemeal, fruit	L	H	F	
Buns, wholemeal, spiced fruit	L	H	F	
Butter, Cornish	H	O	O	plastic tub
Butter, Dutch	O	O	O	silver foil
Butter, English	H	O	O	parchment
Butter, English, Continental taste	O	O	O	parchment
Butter, Normandy	H	O	O	silver foil
Butter, Shropshire	H	O	O	parchment
Butter, Somerset	H	O	O	parchment
Butter, special blend	H	O	O	parchment
Butterscotch	L	H	O	
Cabbage, sliced	O	O	O	frozen

SAINSBURY'S	Salt	Sugar	Flavour	Packaging
Cake covering, milk chocolate flavour	O	H	F	wrap
Cake covering, plain chocolate & orange flavour	O	H	O	wrap
Cake covering, plain chocolate flavour	L	H	F	wrap
Cake mix, chocolate sponge	L	H	F	
Cake mix, rock	O	H	F	
Cake mix, vanilla sponge	L	H	F	
Cake, apple & sultana	L	H	O	
Cake, walnut	L	H	F	
Cakes, Eccles	L	L	O	
Cannelloni, egg	O	O	O	carton
Capelletti	L	O	O	fresh
Capelletti, tomato	L	O	X	fresh
Caramel Creme Surprise (Summer 1986)	X	X	X	
Caramel dessert (Summer 1986)	X	X	X	
Carrots, baby, English	O	O	O	frozen
Carrots, julienne	O	O	O	frozen
Carrots, sliced	L	O	O	can
Carrots, sliced	O	O	O	frozen
Carrots, sliced, in water	O	O	O	can
Carrots, whole	L	O	O	can
Carrots, whole, in water	O	O	O	can

SAINSBURY'S	Salt	Sugar	Flavour	Packaging
Carrots, young	L	L	O	can
Cashew kernels	O	O	O	poly bag
Cauliflower, crispy coated	H	O	F	frozen
Cauliflower, florets	O	O	O	frozen
Cheese & ham nibbles	H	L	O	pre-packed
Cheese, 14% fat	H	O	O	pre-packed
Cheese, Bavarian Brie	H	O	O	pre-packed
Cheese, Bavarian Brie, blue	H	O	O	pre-packed
Cheese, Bavarian Brie with herbs	H	O	O	pre-packed
Cheese, Bavarian Brie with mushrooms	H	O	O	pre-packed
Cheese, Bavarian Brie with peppers	H	O	O	pre-packed
Cheese, Bavarian Emmental	H	O	O	pre-packed
Cheese, Bavarian, smoked	H	O	O	pre-packed
Cheese, Bavarian, smoked & ham	H	O	O	pre-packed
Cheese, Caerphilly	H	O	O	pre-packed
Cheese, Caerphilly, traditional	H	O	O	pre-packed
Cheese, Cheddar with walnuts	H	O	O	pre-packed
Cheese, Cheddar, Australian	H	O	O	pre-packed
Cheese, Cheddar, Canadian	H	O	O	pre-packed
Cheese, Cheddar, Canadian traditional	H	O	O	pre-packed
Cheese, Cheddar, English	H	O	O	pre-packed

SAINSBURY'S	Salt	Sugar	Flavour	Packaging
Cheese, Cheddar, English, coloured	H	0	0	pre-packed
Cheese, Cheddar, English mature	H	0	0	pre-packed
Cheese, Cheddar, English mild	H	0	0	pre-packed
Cheese, Cheddar, farmhouse	H	0	0	pre-packed
Cheese, Cheddar, Irish	H	0	0	pre-packed
Cheese, Cheddar, Scottish	H	0	0	pre-packed
Cheese, Cheddar, Scottish, coloured	H	0	0	pre-packed
Cheese, Cheddar, Somerset	H	0	0	pre-packed
Cheese, Cheddar, vegetarian	H	0	0	pre-packed
Cheese, Cheshire, blue	H	0	0	pre-packed
Cheese, Cheshire, coloured	H	0	0	pre-packed
Cheese, Cheshire, traditional	H	0	0	pre-packed
Cheese, Cheshire, white	H	0	0	pre-packed
Cheese, chèvre blanc	H	0	0	pre-packed
Cheese, cottage	L	0	0	pre-packed
Cheese, cottage, half fat	L	0	0	pre-packed
Cheese, cottage, half fat with pineapple	L	0	0	pre-packed
Cheese, cottage, half fat with vegetables	L	0	0	pre-packed
Cheese, cottage, with chives	H	0	0	pre-packed
Cheese, cottage, with onion & pepper	L	0	0	pre-packed
Cheese, cottage, with pineapple	L	0	0	pre-packed

SAINSBURY'S	Salt	Sugar	Flavour	Packaging
Cheese, cream	L	0	0	pre-packed
Cheese, creamery full fat soft	L	0	0	pre-packed
Cheese, curd	H	0	0	pre-packed
Cheese, Danish blue	H	0	0	pre-packed
Cheese, Derby	H	0	0	pre-packed
Cheese, Derby, sage	H	0	0	pre-packed
Cheese, Dolcelatte	H	0	0	pre-packed
Cheese, double Gloucester	H	0	0	pre-packed
Cheese, double Gloucester with blue stilton	H	0	0	pre-packed
Cheese, double Gloucester with chives & onion	H	0	0	pre-packed
Cheese, double Gloucester with mixed sweet pickle	H	L	0	pre-packed
Cheese, double Gloucester, traditional	H	0	0	pre-packed
Cheese, French Brie	H	0	0	pre-packed
Cheese, French Feta	H	0	0	pre-packed
Cheese, full fat soft with herbs	H	0	0	pre-packed
Cheese, Gorgonzola	H	0	0	pre-packed
Cheese, Jutland blue	H	0	0	sealed tray
Cheese, Lancashire	H	0	0	pre-packed
Cheese, Lancashire, traditional	H	0	0	pre-packed
Cheese, Leicester	H	0	0	pre-packed

137

SAINSBURY'S	Salt	Sugar	Flavour	Packaging
Cheese, Leicester, red with walnuts	H	0	0	pre-packed
Cheese, Leicester, traditional	H	0	0	pre-packed
Cheese, Leiden	H	0	0	pre-packed
Cheese, Normandy Camembert, portions & demi	H	0	0	pre-packed
Cheese, Normandy Camembert, traditional	H	0	0	pre-packed
Cheese, Norwegian Jarlsberg	H	0	0	pre-packed
Cheese, Parmesan	H	0	0	pre-packed
Cheese, Petit Suisse	0	0	0	pre-packed
Cheese, skimmed milk, soft	0	0	0	pre-packed
Cheese, Somerset Brie	H	0	0	pre-packed
Cheese, Stilton, blue	H	0	0	pre-packed
Cheese, Stilton, white	H	0	0	pre-packed
Cheese, Svenbo	H	0	0	pre-packed
Cheese, Swiss Emmental	H	0	0	pre-packed
Cheese, Swiss Gruyère	H	0	0	pre-packed
Cheese, Wensleydale	H	0	0	pre-packed
Cheese, Wensleydale, traditional	H	0	0	pre-packed
Cheesecake, blackcurrant (Summer 1986)	X	X	X	
Cheesecake, strawberry (Summer 1986)	X	X	X	
Chick peas	L	0	0	can
Chicken à la King	X	X	X	can

SAINSBURY'S	Salt	Sugar	Flavour	Packaging
Chicken breast fillets, boneless, roast	L	O	O	chilled
Chicken breast in breadcrumbs	H	O	O	chilled
Chicken breast portions, roast	L	O	O	chilled
Chicken breast roll	X	X	F	pre-packed
Chicken breasts en croûte	H	O	F	chilled
Chicken curry (Autumn 1986)	X	X	X	can
Chicken drumsticks in breadcrumbs	L	O	O	chilled
Chicken drumsticks, roast	L	O	O	chilled
Chicken gratin	X	O	O	frozen
Chicken in white sauce (Autumn 1986)	X	X	X	can
Chicken Kiev	H	O	O	frozen
Chicken leg portions, roast	L	O	O	chilled
Chicken legs, part boned with sav rice sultanas & apple	L	O	O	chilled
Chicken Madras	X	X	X	can
Chicken nibbles (Spring 1986)	H	O	O	
Chicken nuggets in batter	L	L	O	frozen
Chicken nuggets in breadcrumbs	L	L	O	frozen
Chicken paste	H	O	O	jar
Chicken spread	L	O	O	jar
Chicken thighs, roast	L	O	O	chilled

SAINSBURY'S	Salt	Sugar	Flavour	Packaging
Chicken, southern style	H	L	O	chilled
Chicken, whole, roast	L	O	O	chilled
Chilli powder	O	O	O	pot
Chips, crinkle cut	O	O	O	frozen
Chips, oven	O	O	O	frozen
Chips, steak	O	O	O	frozen
Chips, straight cut	O	O	O	frozen
Chocolate buttons, milk	O	H	O	
Chocolate Creme Surprise (Summer 1986)	X	X	X	
Chocolate drops, milk, for cooking	O	H	O	sachet
Chocolate drops, plain, for cooking	O	H	O	sachet
Chocolate eclairs	L	H	O	
Chocolate eclairs, dairy cream	O	H	F	frozen
Chocolate eggs, milk	O	H	O	
Chocolate flakes	O	H	O	pot
Chocolate mint crisp	O	H	O	
Chocolate peppermint cream	O	H	O	
Chocolate spread	O	H	F	plastic tub
Chocolate sugar strands	O	H	O	pot
Chutney, mango	H	H	O	jar
Cinnamon, ground	O	O	O	pot

140

SAINSBURY'S	Salt	Sugar	Flavour	Packaging
Citrus 5 crush	O	H	O	carton
Cloves	O	O	O	pot
Coco snaps	H	H	O	carton
Cocoa	L	O	O	carton
Coconut, desiccated	O	O	O	poly bag
Coconut, sweetened	O	H	O	poly bag
Cod casserole	H	O	O	frozen
Cod fillets	O	O	O	frozen
Cod fillets in golden breadcrumbs	L	O	O	frozen
Cod in seafood sauce	L	O	O	frozen
Cod portions	O	O	O	frozen
Cod portions in crispy batter	H	O	O	frozen
Cod portions in golden breadcrumbs	L	O	O	frozen
Cod, smoked, boil in the bag	H	O	O	frozen
Coffee & chicory mixture	O	O	O	carton
Coffee & chicory powder	O	O	O	carton
Coffee crystals	O	H	O	poly bag
Coffee Plus	O	O	O	jar
Coffee, beans, roasted Continental blend	O	O	O	carton
Coffee, beans, roasted Kenya blend	O	O	O	carton
Coffee, beans, roasted Original blend	O	O	O	carton

SAINSBURY'S	Salt	Sugar	Flavour	Packaging
Coffee, filter Continental roast	0	0	0	carton
Coffee, filter Costa Rica blend	0	0	0	carton
Coffee, filter Kenya blend	0	0	0	carton
Coffee, filter Original blend	0	0	0	carton
Coffee, filter, decaffeinated	0	0	0	carton
Coffee, gold choice Continental	0	0	0	jar
Coffee, gold choice, Continental, freeze dried, instant	0	0	0	jar
Coffee, gold choice, decaff., freeze dried, instant	0	0	0	jar
Coffee, gold choice, freeze dried, instant	0	0	0	jar
Coffee, granules, full roast	0	0	0	jar
Coffee, granules, medium roast	0	0	0	jar
Coffee, instant granules, decaffeinated	0	0	0	jar
Coffee, medium ground Continental roast	0	0	0	carton
Coffee, medium ground Costa Rica blend	0	0	0	carton
Coffee, medium ground Kenya blend	0	0	0	carton
Coffee, medium ground Original blend	0	0	0	carton
Coffee, powder, Brazilian blend	0	0	0	carton
Coffee, powder, instant	0	0	0	carton
Coffee, powder, medium roast	0	0	0	jar
Coffee, premium blend for filters	0	0	0	carton

SAINSBURY'S	Salt	Sugar	Flavour	Packaging
Coffee, premium blend for percolators	O	O	O	carton
Coffee, Viennese, with fig seasoning	O	O	O	carton
Coleslaw	L	L	O	delicatessen
Coley fillets	O	O	O	frozen
Coley portions	O	O	O	frozen
Conserve, apricot	O	H	O	jar
Conserve, blackcurrant	O	H	O	jar
Conserve, raspberry	O	H	O	jar
Conserve, strawberry	O	H	O	jar
Conserve, Swiss black cherry	O	H	O	jar
Corn cobs	O	O	O	frozen
Cornflakes	H	H	O	carton
Cornflakes, honey nut	H	H	O	carton
Cornflour	O	O	O	
Cornish pasties	H	O	O	frozen
Cornish wafers	H	L	O	
Crab paste	L	O	O	jar
Crab spread	L	O	O	jar
Crab, potted	L	L	O	jar
Crackers, snack	H	L	O	
Cream	O	O	O	can

SAINSBURY'S	Salt	Sugar	Flavour	Packaging
Cream, fresh double	O	O	O	chilled
Cream, fresh half	O	O	O	chilled
Cream, fresh single	O	O	O	chilled
Cream, fresh soured	O	O	O	chilled
Cream, fresh whipping	O	O	O	chilled
Cream, fresh, Devonshire clotted	O	O	O	chilled
Crisp, corn	O	H	O	
Crisp, fruit	O	H	F	
Crisp, rice	O	H	F	
Crisps, cream cheese & chive	H	O	F	nine pack
Crisps, mixed flavour	H	O	F	
Crisps, prawn cocktail	H	O	F	nine pack
Crisps, ready salted	H	O	O	six pack
Crisps, ready salted	H	O	O	
Crisps, ready salted	H	O	O	
Crudités with cheese & chives dip	L	O	O	fresh
Crumble, apple & blackberry	O	H	F	frozen
Crunch bars	O	H	O	
Crunchnut topping	L	H	O	poly bag
Crunchy oat cereal	L	H	O	carton
Crunchy oat with bran & apple	L	H	O	carton

SAINSBURY'S	Salt	Sugar	Flavour	Packaging
Cucumber in sour sweet vinegar	L	H	O	jar
Curry powder	O	O	O	pot
Curry powder, Madras style	O	O	O	pot
Curry powder, vindaloo hot	H	O	O	pot
Dates, chopped, sugar rolled	O	H	O	poly bag
Doughnuts, wholemeal	L	H	O	
Dressing, French	H	L	O	jar/bottle
Dressing, Italian	H	L	O	jar/bottle
Dressing, tomato & herb	H	O	O	jar/bottle
Drinking chocolate	L	H	F	tin
Drinking chocolate, fat reduced	L	H	F	plastic jar
Easy pints	O	L	O	plastic bottle
Fish cakes	L	O	O	frozen
Fish cakes, salmon	H	O	O	frozen
Fish fingers, cod fillet	L	O	F	frozen
Fish fingers, cod, economy	L	O	O	frozen
Flan case, golden bake	L	H	O	
Flan, cauliflower cheese	L	L	O	chilled, carton
Flan, cheese & onion	L	L	O	chilled, carton
Flour, plain	O	O	O	
Flour, self raising	O	O	O	

SAINSBURY'S	Salt	Sugar	Flavour	Packaging
Flour, stoneground wholemeal	O	O	O	
Flour, strong white	O	O	O	
Fromage frais with apricot	O	L	F	jar
Fromage frais with strawberry	O	L	F	jar
Fruit cocktail drink	X	H	O	chilled, carton
Fruit trifle, fresh cream (Summer 1986)	L	X	X	
Fudge, dairy	O	H	O	pot
Garlic, chopped	O	O	O	pot
Ginger, ground	O	O	O	
Ginger, stem	O	H	O	jar
Golden syrup	O	H	O	plastic jar
Grapefruit juice, pure	O	O	O	chilled, carton
Grapefruit juice, pure jaffa	O	O	O	carton
Grapefruit segments in syrup	O	L	O	can
Grapefruit segments, flavourseal, in natural juice	O	O	O	can
Haddock fillets	O	O	O	frozen
Haddock fillets in golden breadcrumbs	L	O	O	frozen
Haddock fillets, smoked	H	O	O	frozen
Haddock golden cutlets with butter, boil in the bag	H	O	O	frozen
Haddock goujons, smoked	H	O	O	frozen

SAINSBURY'S	Salt	Sugar	Flavour	Packaging
Haddock portions	O	O	O	frozen
Haddock portions in golden batter	H	O	O	frozen
Haddock portions in golden breadcrumbs	L	O	O	frozen
Hash browns	L	O	O	frozen
Hawaiian cocktail drink	O	H	O	chilled, carton
Hazelnut kernels	O	O	O	poly bag
Hazelnuts, chopped roast	O	L	O	poly bag
Herb thins	H	O	O	
Herbs (9 individual varieties)	O	O	O	pot
Herbs, mixed	O	O	O	pot
Herring fillets, marinated	H	O	O	pre-packed
Hoagies, wholemeal rolls	H	L	L	
Honey comb crunch, milk chocolate	O	H	F	
Honey double dessert (Summer 1986)	X	X	X	
Honey, acacia	O	O	O	jar
Honey, clear, blended	O	O	O	jar
Honey, cut comb	O	O	O	jar
Honey, set, blended	O	O	O	jar
Honey, set, Canadian	O	O	O	jar
Horseradish, creamed (Summer 1986)	X	X	X	
Houmous	H	O	O	delicatessen

SAINSBURY'S	Salt	Sugar	Flavour	Packaging
Instant oats	L	H	O	carton
Instant oats with bran	L	H	O	carton
Irish stew (Autumn 1986)	X	X	X	can
Island sun drink	O	H	O	carton
Jacket scallops, oven	O	O	O	frozen
Jaffa orange juice, pure	O	O	O	carton
Jam, pure fruit, apricot	O	H	O	jar
Jam, pure fruit, black cherry	O	H	O	jar
Jam, pure fruit, raspberry	O	H	O	jar
Jam, pure fruit, red cherry	O	H	O	jar
Jam, pure fruit, strawberry	O	H	O	jar
Jamaican cocktail drink	O	H	O	chilled, carton
Kipper fillets, ready to eat	H	O	O	pre-packed
Kippers with butter, boned, boil in the bag	H	O	O	frozen
Krispwheat	H	O	O	
Krispwheat, wholemeal	L	O	O	frozen, carton
Lasagne	O	O	O	carton
Lasagne, egg	O	O	O	carton
Lasagne, verdi	O	O	O	carton
Lemon crush, traditional	O	H	O	carton
Lemon curd (Summer 1986)	O	H	O	jar

SAINSBURY'S	Salt	Sugar	Flavour	Packaging
Lentils	O	O	O	poly bag
Macaroni	O	O	O	poly bag
Macaroni cheese (Autumn 1986)	X	X	X	can
Macaroni, quick cook	O	O	O	poly bag
Mackerel, Cornish, in brine	L	L	O	can
Mackerel, Cornish, in tomato sauce	L	O	O	can
Mackerel, fillets in brine	H	O	O	can
Mackerel, fillets in tomato sauce	L	L	O	can
Mackerel, peppered, boil in the bag	H	O	O	frozen
Mackerel, smoked	H	O	O	pre-packed
Mackerel, smoked, peppered	H	O	O	pre-packed
Malted drink	L	H	F	jar
Mandarin orange segments in light syrup	O	H	O	can
Mandarin orange segments in light syrup (broken)	O	H	O	can
Mandarin orange segments in natural juice, unsweetened	O	O	O	can
Margarine, blue label	H	O	F	packet
Margarine, green label	H	O	F	
Margarine, soft, blue label	H	O	F	tub
Margarine, soya	H	O	F	

SAINSBURY'S	Salt	Sugar	Flavour	Packaging
Margarine, sunflower	H	O	F	
Marmalade, fresh fruit, grapefruit	O	H	O	jar
Marmalade, fresh fruit, lemon & lime	O	H	O	jar
Marmalade, fresh fruit, sweet orange	O	H	O	jar
Marmalade, lemon shred	O	H	O	jar
Marmalade, orange shred	O	H	O	jar
Marmalade, Seville orange	O	H	O	jar
Marzipan, white	O	H	O	silver wrap
Meringue nests	O	O	O	
Milk, evaporated	O	O	O	can
Milk, fresh pasteurised	O	O	O	chilled
Milk, fresh pasteurised, homogenised	O	O	O	chilled
Milk, fresh pasteurised, semi-skimmed	O	O	O	chilled
Milk, fresh pasteurised, skimmed	O	O	O	chilled
Milk, skimmed (dried)	L	O	O	carton
Mincemeat	O	I	O	
Mini wheats	O	I	O	carton
Mint imperials	O	I	O	
Mints, after dinner	O	I	O	
Mints, chewy	O	I	O	
Mints, extra strong	O	I	O	

SAINSBURY'S	Salt	Sugar	Flavour	Packaging
Mints, soft	O	H	O	poly bag
Mixed fruit	L	O	O	4 pack
Mousse, chocolate (Summer 1986)	L	H	O	frozen
Mousse, haddock & spinach	L	O	O	carton
Muesli, bran	O	L	O	carton
Muesli, deluxe	L	O	O	carton
Muffins, wholemeal	L	L	O	
Muffins, wholemeal, raisin	H	O	F	frozen
Mushrooms, crispy coated	O	O	O	
Mushrooms, dried	L	O	O	can
Mushrooms, sliced	L	O	O	can
Mushrooms, whole	L	O	O	can
Mushrooms, whole, button	H	O	O	delicatessen
Mussels in tomato sauce	H	O	O	jar/bottle
Mustard with peppercorns	H	O	O	jar/bottle
Mustard, coarse ground	H	O	O	jar/bottle
Mustard, Dijon	X	X	X	
Mustard, English (Summer 1986)	O	O	O	bag
Natural bran	O	O	O	pot
Nutmeg, ground	O	O	O	poly bag
Nuts, chopped, mixed	O	O	O	

SAINSBURY'S	Salt	Sugar	Flavour	Packaging
Nuts, salted mixed	H	O	O	carton
Oats & bran flakes	H	H	O	carton
Oats with bran	O	O	O	
Oil, blended vegetable	O	O	O	plastic bottle
Oil, corn	O	O	O	plastic bottle
Oil, extra virgin olive	O	O	O	plastic bottle
Oil, groundnut	O	O	O	plastic bottle
Oil, olive	O	O	O	plastic bottle
Oil, safflower	O	O	O	plastic bottle
Oil, soya	O	O	O	plastic bottle
Oil, sunflower	O	O	O	plastic bottle
Olives in brine	H	O	O	delicatessen
Olives, pitted green	H	O	O	jar
Olives, stuffed green	H	O	O	jar
Olives, whole green	H	O	O	jar
Orange juice	O	O	O	can
Orange juice, freshly squeezed	O	O	O	chilled, bottle
Orange juice, pure	O	O	O	chilled, carton
Orange juice, pure	O	O	O	carton
Orange segments in natural juice, unsweetened	O	O	O	can
Oriental drink	O	H	O	carton

SAINSBURY'S	Salt	Sugar	Flavour	Packaging
Paglia e fieno	O	O	O	fresh
Paprika	O	O	O	pot
Passata	L	O	O	can
Pasta quills	O	O	O	carton/pouch pack
Pasta shells	O	L	O	carton/pouch pack
Pasta shells in spicy tomato sauce	L	L	O	can
Pasta spirals	O	O	O	carton/pouch pack
Pasta whirls	L	O	O	carton/pouch pack
Pastry, puff	L	L	O	chilled
Pastry, puff	L	O	O	frozen
Pastry, shortcrust	L	L	O	frozen
Pastry, wholemeal	H	O	O	chilled
Pasty, chunky fresh vegetable	H	O	O	chilled, film wrap
Pasty, potato, cheese & onion	H	O	O	chilled, film wrap
Pâté, chicken liver with red wine	H	O	O	pre-packed
Pâté, duck & orange, low fat	H	O	O	delicatessen
Pâté, farmhouse, low fat	L	O	O	delicatessen
Pâté, vegetable	O	O	O	delicatessen
Peach halves in fruit juice, unsweetened	O	O	O	can
Peach halves in syrup	O	H	O	can
Peach slices in fruit juice, unsweetened	O	O	O	can.

SAINSBURY'S	Salt	Sugar	Flavour	Packaging
Peach slices in syrup	O	H	O	can
Peanut brittle	L	H	O	jar
Peanut butter, coarse	L	L	O	jar
Peanut butter, smooth	L	L	O	jar
Peanuts & raisins	O	O	O	can
Pear halves in fruit juice, unsweetened	O	O	O	can
Pear halves in syrup	O	H	O	can
Pear quarters in fruit juice, unsweetened	O	O	O	can
Pear quarters in syrup	O	H	O	can
Peas, dried	O	O	O	poly bag
Peas, economy	O	O	O	frozen
Peas, garden	O	O	O	frozen
Peas, garden (Autumn 1986)	X	X	X	can
Peas, garden, in water	O	O	O	can
Peas, minted	O	L	O	frozen
Peas, processed (Autumn 1986)	X	X	X	can
Pease pudding	L	O	O	can
Pepper, black, ground	O	O	O	pot
Pepper, white, ground	O	O	O	pot
Peppercorns, black, whole	O	O	O	pot
Peppermint flavour	O	O	O	miniature bottle

SAINSBURY'S	Salt	Sugar	Flavour	Packaging
Petits pois	O	O	O	frozen
Petits pois	L	L	O	can
Pie, bramley apple	O	H	O	frozen
Pie, cod & broccoli	L	O	F	frozen
Pie, cod & prawn	L	O	O	frozen
Pie, smoked haddock	L	O	O	frozen
Pie, vegetable	L	O	O	frozen
Pies, bramley apple	L	H	O	
Pies, bramley apple, wholemeal	L	H	O	
Pilchards, Cornish, in brine	L	O	O	can
Pilchards, Cornish, in tomato sauce	O	O	O	can
Pineapple juice, pure	O	O	O	chilled, carton
Pineapple juice, pure	O	O	O	carton
Pineapple pieces in natural juice, unsweetened	O	O	O	can
Pineapple pieces in syrup	O	H	O	can
Pineapple slices in natural juice, unsweetened	O	O	O	can
Pineapple slices in syrup	O	H	O	can
Pineapple, crushed, in syrup	L	H	O	can
Pizza flan, Chilli con Carne, premium deep filled	L	L	O	chilled, carton
Pizza snacks, cheese & tomato	H	L	O	frozen, poly bag × 8

SAINSBURY'S	Salt	Sugar	Flavour	Packaging
Pizza, cheese & onion	L	L	0	frozen, poly bag × 4
Pizza, cheese & tomato	H	L	0	chilled, film wrap
Pizza, cheese & tomato	L	L	0	frozen, poly bag × 4
Pizza, cheese & tomato with mixed veg on brown base	L	L	0	chilled, film wrap
Pizza, cheese & tomato, pan baked	L	L	0	chilled, film wrap
Pizza, cheese, tomato & mushroom	H	L	0	chilled, film wrap
Pizza, cheese, tomato with peppers & mushroom	H	L	0	chilled, film wrap
Pizza, French bread, cheese & tomato	L	L	0	frozen, carton
Pizza, tropical fruit & nut	L	L	0	chilled, film wrap
Plaice fillets	O	O	0	frozen
Plaice fillets with golden breadcrumbs	L	O	0	frozen
Plaice fillets, whole in golden breadcrumbs	L	O	0	frozen
Plaice, stuffed with prawn & mushroom filling	H	L	0	frozen
Plums, golden, in syrup (Autumn 1986)	X	X	X	can
Pork sausagemeat plait with apple	L	L	0	frozen
Pork, leg, roast	X	X	0	pre-packed
Potato croquettes	L	O	0	frozen
Potatoes, new	L	L	0	can

SAINSBURY'S	Salt	Sugar	Flavour	Packaging
Potatoes, new, Jersey	L	L	O	can
Potatoes, sliced, Jersey	L	L	O	can
Prawns, peeled, Norwegian	H	O	O	frozen
Prawns, peeled, Scottish	H	O	O	frozen
Preserve, ginger	O	H	O	jar
Prunes	O	O	O	poly bag
Prunes in fruit juice, unsweetened	O	O	O	can
Prunes in syrup	O	H	O	can
Prunes, ready to eat	O	O	O	poly bag
Puffed wheat	O	O	O	carton
Quarterpounders	L	O	O	frozen
Quiche, cheese & asparagus	L	O	O	frozen
Quiche, spinach	L	O	O	delicatessen
Quiche, tomato & olive	L	O	O	delicatessen
Raisins & mixed nuts	O	O	O	frozen
Raisins, seedless	O	O	O	poly bag
Raisins, seedless, Kings Ruby	O	O	O	poly bag
Raisins, stoned	O	O	O	poly bag
Raspberries, in juice (Autumn 1986)	X	X	X	can
Raspberries, in syrup (Autumn 1986)	X	X	X	can
Ratatouille Provençale	L	L	O	can

SAINSBURY'S

SAINSBURY'S	Salt	Sugar	Flavour	Packaging
Ravioli	L	O	O	fresh
Ravioli in tomato sauce (Autumn 1986)	X	X	X	can
Redcurrant jelly	O	H	O	jar
Rice pops	H	H	O	carton
Rice, American easy cook	O	O	O	poly bag
Rice, Basmati	O	O	O	poly bag
Rice, boil in the bag	O	O	O	carton
Rice, boil in the bag, brown	O	O	O	carton
Rice, brown	O	O	O	poly bag
Rice, creamed	O	H	O	can
Rice, flaked	O	O	O	poly bag
Rice, for puddings	O	O	O	poly bag
Rice, ground	O	O	O	poly bag
Rice, Italian easy cook	O	O	O	poly bag
Rice, Italian easy cook, brown	O	O	O	poly bag
Rice, Italian risotto	O	O	O	poly bag
Rice, long grain	O	O	O	poly bag
Rolls, wholemeal	H	L	O	
Salad cream (Summer 1986)	X	X	X	fresh
Salad, apple & raisin with walnuts	O	O	O	
Salad, apple, peach & nut with coconut	L	L	O	delicatessen

SAINSBURY'S	Salt	Sugar	Flavour	Packaging
Salad, Chinese leaf & sweetcorn	O	O	O	fresh
Salad, celery, peanut & sultana	L	O	O	delicatessen
Salad, cracked wheat & mint	O	O	O	delicatessen
Salad, crisp vegetable	H	L	O	delicatessen
Salad, Eastern	L	O	O	delicatessen
Salad, fennel & watercress	O	O	O	fresh
Salad, four bean	L	L	O	delicatessen
Salad, fresh fruit	O	O	O	delicatessen
Salad, Greek	L	L	O	delicatessen
Salad, mild curry rice	L	L	O	delicatessen
Salad, mixed	H	L	O	delicatessen
Salad, pasta & olive	L	O	O	delicatessen
Salad, pepper	L	O	O	can
Salad, potato in fresh mayonnaise	L	L	O	delicatessen
Salad, potato with chives	L	O	O	delicatessen
Salad, rice & vegetable	L	O	O	delicatessen
Salad, spinach & chick pea	O	O	O	delicatessen
Salmon & shrimp paste	L	O	O	jar
Salmon spread	L	O	O	jar
Salmon, medium red	L	O	O	can
Salmon, pink	L	O	O	can

SAINSBURY'S	Salt	Sugar	Flavour	Packaging
Salmon, potted	L	L	O	jar
Salmon, red	L	O	O	can
Salmon, smoked, sliced	H	O	O	pre-packed
Salt, celery	X	X	X	jar
Salt, cooking	H	O	O	various
Salt, table	H	O	O	various
Samosas, lamb	H	O	O	delicatessen
Samosas, vegetable	H	O	O	delicatessen
Sardine & tomato paste	L	O	O	jar
Sardine & tomato spread	L	O	O	jar
Sardines in brine	L	O	O	can
Sardines in oil	L	O	O	can
Sardines in olive oil	L	O	O	can
Sardines in tomato sauce	L	O	O	can
Sauce for cooking, red wine	O	L	O	can
Sauce for cooking, sweet & sour	H	H	O	can
Sauce, Bolognaise	H	L	O	pre-packed
Sauce, Bolognese	X	L	O	can
Sauce, bread	O	X	X	box
Sauce, caramel	O	H	O	
Sauce, chocolate	O	H	O	

SAINSBURY'S	Salt	Sugar	Flavour	Packaging
Sauce, cranberry	O	H	O	jar
Sauce, horseradish, creamed	H	H	O	jar
Sauce, pasta, tomato	H	L	O	pre-packed
Sauce, pour over, Bonne Femme	L	O	O	frozen
Sausage rolls, cocktail	H	O	O	frozen, carton
Sausage rolls, large	H	O	O	frozen, carton
Sausage rolls, lattice topped cheese pastry, thaw & eat	H	O	O	frozen, carton
Sausage rolls, party size	H	O	O	frozen, poly bag
Sausages, extra quality	H	L	O	chilled
Scallops, breaded	L	O	O	frozen
Scampi, breaded	L	O	O	frozen
Scones, wholemeal, fruit	L	H	O	
Scottish oat flakes	O	O	O	poly bag
Seafood platter, breaded	L	O	O	frozen
Semolina	O	O	O	poly bag
Snowflakes	H	H	O	carton
Soup, cream of tomato	L	L	O	can
Soup, tomato	L	L	O	can
Spaghetti	O	O	O	cellophane wrap
Spaghetti in tomato sauce	H	L	O	can

SAINSBURY'S	Salt	Sugar	Flavour	Packaging
Spaghetti rings	H	L	O	can
Spaghetti, Italian quick cook	O	O	O	cellophane wrap
Spaghetti, numberelli	H	L	O	can
Spaghetti, wholewheat	H	O	O	cellophane wrap
Spanahopitta	O	O	O	delicatessen
Spice, ground mixed	O	O	O	pot
Spice, pickling	O	O	O	pot
Spinach, chopped	L	O	F	frozen
Sponge bar, black cherry & buttercream	L	H	O	
Sponge fingers	H	H	F	tub
Spread, low fat	H	O	F	tub
Spread, low fat, sunflower	O	O	O	frozen
Sprouts, button	X	X	X	can
Steak, stewed in gravy (Autumn 1986)	O	O	O	fresh
Stir fry vegetables	X	X	X	can
Strawberries in juice (Autumn 1986)	X	X	X	can
Strawberries in syrup (Autumn 1986)	H	O	O	box
Stuffing mix, parsley, thyme & lemon	H	O	O	box
Stuffing mix, sage & onion	O	O	O	
Suet	O	H	O	
Sugar, caster	O		O	paper bag

SAINSBURY'S	Salt	Sugar	Flavour	Packaging
Sugar, dark brown, soft	O	H	O	poly bag
Sugar, Demerara	O	H	O	poly bag
Sugar, granulated	O	H	O	paper bag
Sugar, granulated, golden	O	H	O	poly bag
Sugar, icing	O	H	O	carton
Sugar, light brown, soft	O	H	O	poly bag
Sugar, Muscovado	O	H	O	poly bag
Sugar, small cube	O	H	O	box
Sultana bran	H	H	O	carton
Swede, diced	O	O	O	frozen
Sweetcorn	L	L	O	frozen
Sweetcorn & peppers	O	O	O	can
Sweetcorn & peppers	L	L	O	frozen
Sweetcorn, whole kernel	L	L	O	can
Swiss roll, apricot	L	H	F	
Swiss roll, bramley apple	L	H	F	
Swiss roll, super chocolate	L	H	F	
Tagliatelle	O	O	O	fresh
Tagliatelle verdi	O	O	O	carton
Tagliatelle, egg	O	O	O	carton
Tagliatelle, egg & spinach	O	O	O	carton

SAINSBURY'S	Salt	Sugar	Flavour	Packaging
Tapioca	O	O	O	poly bag
Tart, apple dessert	L	H	O	
Tea bags, Assam blend	O	O	O	packet
Tea bags, brown label	O	O	O	packet
Tea bags, Ceylon blend	O	O	O	packet
Tea bags, Earl Grey	O	O	O	packet
Tea bags, Kenya blend	O	O	O	packet
Tea bags, red label	O	O	O	packet
Tea, Assam blend	O	O	O	packet
Tea, brown label	O	O	O	packet
Tea, Ceylon blend	O	O	O	packet
Tea, China & Darjeeling	O	O	O	packet
Tea, Earl Grey	O	O	O	packet
Tea, Kenya blend	O	O	O	packet
Tea, red label	O	O	O	packet
Teacakes, wholemeal	L	L	O	
Terrine, vegetable	L	O	O	delicatessen
Toffee	O	H	O	× 3 roll pack
Toffee bon bons	L	H	F	
Toffee popcorn	L	H	O	
Toffee, mint	L	H	O	× 3 roll pack

SAINSBURY'S	Salt	Sugar	Flavour	Packaging
Toffees, Devon	L	H	F	
Tomato juice	L	O	O	can
Tomato ketchup	H	H	O	bottle
Tomato ketchup, Italian	H	H	O	bottle
Tomato purée, double concentrate	O	O	O	can
Tomatoes, chopped	L	O	O	can
Tortelloni	L	O	O	fresh
Tortelloni, spinach	L	O	O	fresh
Tortilla chips	H	O	O	
Tropical fruit drink	O	H	O	carton
Trout, rainbow	O	O	O	frozen
Tuna & mayonnaise spread	L	O	O	jar
Tuna chunks in brine	X	X	X	can
Tuna chunks in oil	X	X	X	can
Tuna, South Seas in brine	L	O	O	can
Tuna, South Seas in vegetable oil	L	O	O	can
Tuna, skipjack in brine	L	O	O	can
Tuna, skipjack in oil	L	O	O	can
Turkey breast	X	X	O	pre-packed
Turkey breast joint, roast	H	O	O	frozen
Turkey breast slices, roast	X	X	F	delicatessen

SAINSBURY'S	Salt	Sugar	Flavour	Packaging
Turkey breast, cooked	H	0	0	pre-packed
Turkey breast, smoked	H	0	0	pre-packed
Turkey escalopes in breadcrumbs	L	0	0	tray
Turkey, potted	H	0	F	jar
Turmeric	0	0	0	pot
Twiglets	H	0	0	
Tzatziki	H	0	0	delicatessen
Vegetables, mixed	L	0	0	can
Vegetables, mixed	0	0	0	frozen
Vegetables, mixed, country style	0	0	0	frozen
Vegetables, mixed, special	0	0	0	frozen
Vegetables, stewpack	0	0	0	frozen
Vermicelli, egg	0	0	0	carton
Vine leaves, stuffed	L	0	0	delicatessen
Vinegar, cider	0	0	0	bottle
Vinegar, red wine	0	0	0	bottle
Vinegar, white wine	0	0	0	bottle
Vitapint	0	L	0	chilled
Waffles	L	0	0	frozen
Walnut pieces	0	0	0	poly bag
Water, mineral, Cwm Dale spring, carbonated	0	0	0	bottle

SAINSBURY'S	Salt	Sugar	Flavour	Packaging
Water, mineral, Cwm Dale spring, natural	O	O	O	bottle
Water, mineral, naturally sparkling	O	O	O	bottle
Water, mineral, Scottish spring, carbonated	O	O	O	bottle
Water, mineral, Scottish spring, natural	O	O	O	bottle
Water, soda	H	O	O	bottle
Wheat flakes	O	O	O	carton
Whiting fillets	H	L	O	frozen
Wholemeal thins	H	L	O	
Wholewheat bisk	L	L	O	carton
Yeast	O	O	O	
Yeast extract	O	O	O	jar
Yogurt mousse, strawberry (Summer 1986)	X	X	X	
Yogurt mousse, tropical (Summer 1986)	X	X	X	
Yogurt sundae, black cherry (Summer 1986)	X	X	X	
Yogurt sundae, strawberry (Summer 1986)	X	X	X	
Yogurt, low fat set, real French recipe, apricot	O	H	F	4 pack, chilled
Yogurt, low fat set, real French recipe, exotic fruits	O	H	F	4 pack, chilled
Yogurt, low fat set, real French recipe, fruits of forest	O	H	F	4 pack, chilled
Yogurt, low fat set, real French recipe, kiwi	O	H	F	4 pack, chilled

SAINSBURY'S	Salt	Sugar	Flavour	Packaging
Yogurt, low fat set, real French recipe, lemon	O	H	F	4 pack, chilled
Yogurt, low fat set, real French recipe, raspberry	O	H	F	4 pack, chilled
Yogurt, low fat set, real French recipe, strawberry	O	H	F	4 pack, chilled
Yogurt, low fat set, real French recipe, vanilla	O	H	F	4 pack, chilled
Yogurt, low fat, apricot & mango	O	H	F	4 pack, chilled
Yogurt, low fat, black cherry	O	H	F	chilled
Yogurt, low fat, blueberry & blackberry	O	H	F	4 pack, chilled
Yogurt, low fat, Caribbean	O	H	F	4 pack, chilled
Yogurt, low fat, fruits of the forest	O	H	F	chilled
Yogurt, low fat, hazelnut	O	H	F	chilled
Yogurt, low fat, hazelnut, pistachio & chocolate	O	H	F	chilled
Yogurt, low fat, Mr Forgetful, black cherry	O	H	F	chilled
Yogurt, low fat, Mr Funny, peach melba	O	H	F	chilled
Yogurt, low fat, Mr Greedy, strawberry	O	H	F	chilled
Yogurt, low fat, Mr Happy, banana	O	H	F	chilled
Yogurt, low fat, Mr Lazy, fudge	O	H	F	chilled
Yogurt, low fat, Mr Messy, raspberry	O	H	F	chilled
Yogurt, low fat, Mr Uppity, chocolate	O	H	F	chilled
Yogurt, low fat, mix 'n' crunch	O	O	O	chilled
Yogurt, low fat, natural	O	O	O	chilled
Yogurt, low fat, peach & guava	O	H	F	4 pack, chilled

SAINSBURY'S	Salt	Sugar	Flavour	Packaging
Yogurt, low fat, peach melba	0	H	F	chilled
Yogurt, low fat, plum	0	H	F	chilled
Yogurt, low fat, raspberry & redcurrant	0	H	F	chilled
Yogurt, low fat, rhubarb	0	H	F	chilled
Yogurt, low fat, strawberry	0	H	F	chilled
Yogurt, low fat, tropical fruits	0	H	F	4 pack, chilled
Yogurt, set, Dairy Farm natural	0	0	0	chilled

NOTES

Tesco is particularly concerned about the issues of food and health. In January 1985 Tesco was the first major company to announce that it was labelling all its brand products with nutrition information. Tesco also runs a dietary information service and advises a number of organizations representing sufferers of certain conditions (e.g., The Coeliac Society).

Tesco has been aware for sometime that customers are becoming more concerned about the use of additives in their food. Much of the concern would appear to stem from a lack of understanding, not helped by the sometimes difficult terminology employed. For example, E300 sounds awful, it's chemical name L-ascorbic acid sounds little better but it is actually Vitamin C! It is important to remember that without certain additives, such as preservatives, which prevent food from spoiling rapidly, we would not enjoy the variety and range of foods to which we have become accustomed. It would not be proper to regard all additives as being necessarily suspect.

The following action is being taken:

1   Tesco is reducing the number of additives in foods where possible, concentrating historically on the removal of tartrazine from products such as yogurts and squashes. Additionally, Tesco is extremely careful to ensure that unnecessary additives are not included in their products.

2   Further to this Tesco has compiled a priority list of additives on which their technologists will concentrate,

including artificial colours, benzoate preservatives, BHA and BHT. This list has been compiled after consideration of the Ministry of Agriculture's 'B' list (i.e. those additives over which there is a question mark); additives banned in the USA; Hyperactive Support Group's list of suspect additives, and after discussion with the Leatherhead Food Research Association; the Great Ormond Street Hospital for Sick Children; the British Dietetic Association.

3   This is seen as the beginning of a long term programme where the use of additives in all products will be reviewed.

4   A free guide on additives will be available in Tesco Stores next year as part of the series of Healthy Eating leaflets. It will explain the issues and Tesco's policy with the aim of broadening customers' understanding.

TESCO	Salt	Sugar	Flavour	Packaging
After dinner mints	O	H	O	
Almond flavouring	O	O	O	
Apple juice	O	O	O	long life
Apple juice, English	O	O	O	long life
Apple juice, pure	O	O	O	chilled
Apples, stewed, Dutch	O	H	O	can
Apricots in natural juice	O	O	O	can
Baking powder	O	O	O	
Barley, pearl	L	L	O	
Beans, baked in tomato sauce	O	O	O	can
Beans, black-eye	O	O	O	dried
Beans, broad	L	O	O	frozen
Beans, broad	O	O	O	jar
Beans, butter	L	O	O	dried
Beans, green, cut	L	O	O	jar
Beans, green, fine whole	O	O	O	frozen
Beans, green, sliced	O	O	O	frozen
Beans, green, whole	L	O	O	can
Beans, haricot	O	O	O	dried
Beans, mung	O	O	O	dried
Beans, red kidney	L	L	O	can

173

TESCO	Salt	Sugar	Flavour	Packaging
Beans, red kidney	O	O	O	dried
Beef suet, shredded	O	O	O	
Beetroot, sliced	O	O	O	
Beetroot, whole	O	O	O	
Bicarbonate of Soda	O	O	O	
Bran crunch with banana	L	H	O	
Branflakes	H	H	O	
Branflakes with sultana	H	H	O	
Brazil, milk chocolate	O	H	O	
Brazil, plain chocolate	O	H	O	
Bread baps, wholemeal stoneground	L	L	O	
Bread, natural white loaf	L	O	O	
Bread, stoneground wholemeal	L	L	O	
Bread, wholemeal batch	L	L	O	
Bread, wholemeal pitta	L	O	O	
Bread, wholemeal sliced	L	L	O	
Bread, wholemeal uncut	L	L	O	
Breakfast bran cereal	H	H	O	
Brocolli spears	O	O	O	frozen
Brussels sprouts	O	O	O	frozen
Brussels sprouts, button	O	O	O	frozen

TESCO	Salt	Sugar	Flavour	Packaging
Butter, all types	H	O	O	
Cake covering, milk chocolate	L	H	F	
Cake covering, plain chocolate	O	H	F	
Cake covering, white chocolate	O	H	F	
Caribbean drink	O	H	O	chilled
Carrots, all cuts	L	O	O	can
Carrots, baby	O	O	O	frozen
Carrots, baby	H	L	O	jar
Carrots, baby, whole	O	O	O	frozen
Carrots, baby, whole	L	L	O	can
Cauliflower florets	O	O	O	frozen
Cauliflower florets, fresh	O	O	O	frozen
Cheese spread with onion	L	O	O	
Cheese spread with prawns	L	O	O	
Cheese spread, 6 portions	L	O	O	
Cheese spread, natural	L	O	O	
Cheese spread, Swiss Gruyère	H	O	O	
Cheese, Bavarian Brie	H	O	O	
Cheese, Bavarian Brie with herbs	H	O	O	
Cheese, Bavarian Brie with mushroom	H	O	O	
Cheese, Bavarian Brie with peppers	H	O	O	

TESCO	Salt	Sugar	Flavour	Packaging
Cheese, Brie regal	H	O	O	
Cheese, Caerphilly	L	O	O	
Cheese, Camembert	H	O	O	
Cheese, Cheddar with beer, garlic & parsley	H	O	O	
Cheese, Cheddar, all countries	H	O	O	
Cheese, Cheddar, applewood smoked	H	O	O	
Cheese, Cheddar, coloured	H	L	O	
Cheese, Cheddar, reduced fat	L	O	O	
Cheese, Cheddar, vegetarian	H	O	O	
Cheese, Crediou with walnuts	H	O	O	
Cheese, chèvre (goat)	L	O	O	
Cheese, cottage, natural	L	O	O	
Cheese, cottage, soft dairy	L	O	O	
Cheese, cottage, with Cheddar	L	O	O	
Cheese, cottage, with onion & chives	L	O	O	
Cheese, cottage, with pineapple	L	O	O	
Cheese, curd, medium fat	H	O	O	
Cheese, Danish blue gold	H	O	O	
Cheese, double Gloucester	H	O	O	
Cheese, double Gloucester & Stilton	H	O	O	
Cheese, double Gloucester with onion and chives	H	O	O	

TESCO	Salt	Sugar	Flavour	Packaging
Cheese, Edam	H	O	O	
Cheese, Emmental	L	O	O	
Cheese, French Brie	H	O	O	
Cheese, Gouda	H	O	O	
Cheese, Gruyère	H	O	O	
Cheese, Italian Dolcelatte	H	O	O	
Cheese, Lancashire	H	O	O	
Cheese, Parmesan	H	O	O	
Cheese, Port Salut	H	O	O	
Cheese, red Cheshire	H	O	O	
Cheese, red Leicester	H	O	O	
Cheese, roulé with herbs & garlic	L	O	O	
Cheese, Scottish Cheddar, coloured	L	O	O	
Cheese, St Paulin	L	O	O	
Cheese, Stilton	H	O	O	
Cheese, skimmed milk	O	O	O	
Cheese, smoked Bavarian	H	O	O	
Cheese, soft dairy with chives	H	O	O	
Cheese, soft dairy with pineapple	H	O	O	
Cheese, Wensleydale	L	O	O	
Chick peas	O	O	O	dried

TESCO	Salt	Sugar	Flavour	Packaging
Chicken curry, extra hot	L	L	O	can
Chicken roll, sliced	H	O	O	pre-packed
Chicken, roasted, portion	L	O	O	chilled
Chips, oven	O	O	O	frozen
Chips, steakhouse	O	O	O	frozen
Chips, straight cut	O	O	O	frozen
Chocolate & hazelnut spread	O	O	F	
Chocolate almond cluster	L	H	O	
Chocolate drink	O	H	F	
Chocolate drops, milk	O	H	O	
Chocolate drops, plain	O	H	O	
Chocolate hazelnut cluster	O	H	O	
Chocolate mint cream	O	H	O	
Chocolate mint sticks	O	H	O	
Chocolate peanut cluster	O	H	O	
Chutney, apricot	H	H	O	
Chutney, curried fruit	H	O	O	
Cinnamon	O	O	O	
Cockles	O	H	O	frozen
Cocoa puffs	H	O	O	
Coconut, desiccated	O	O	O	

TESCO	Salt	Sugar	Flavour	Packaging
Coconut, sweetened tenderized	L	H	O	
Cod Bon Femme	L	L	O	frozen
Cod Provençal	L	L	O	frozen
Coffee, all types	O	O	O	
Conserve, apricot	O	H	O	jar
Conserve, black cherry	O	H	O	jar
Conserve, blackcurrant	O	H	O	jar
Conserve, raspberry	O	H	O	jar
Conserve, strawberry	O	H	O	jar
Corn on the cob	O	O	O	frozen
Cornflakes	H	H	O	
Cornflakes, honey & nut	H	H	O	
Cornflour	O	O	O	
Courgettes, sliced	O	O	O	frozen
Cream of tartar	O	O	O	
Cream, clotted, Cornish	O	O	O	
Cream, clotted, Devon	O	O	O	
Cream, double	O	O	O	
Cream, extra thick	O	O	O	
Cream, half	O	O	O	
Cream, single	O	O	O	

TESCO	Salt	Sugar	Flavour	Packaging
Cream, soured	O	O	O	
Cream, sterilized	O	O	O	can
Cream, thick double with rum	O	H	O	
Cream, whipping	H	O	F	
Crisp corn	L	H	F	
Crisp rice	H	H	O	
Crispbread, new style	H	L	O	
Crispbread, whole rye	H	L	O	
Crisps, curry	O	O	O	
Crunch-nut topping	H	H	O	
Cucumber, dill	O	L	O	
Currants, washed	H	O	O	dried
Curry powder, Korma	H	O	O	
Curry powder, Madras	O	O	O	
Dates, chopped, sugar rolled	O	H	O	dried
Dessert sauce, caramel	O	H	O	
Dessert sauce, chocolate	O	H	F	
Dressing, 1000 Island	O	H	O	
Dressing, classic French	H	L	O	
Dressing, Italian garlic	O	O	O	
Dressing, mustard vinaigrette	H	L	O	

TESCO	Salt	Sugar	Flavour	Packaging
Fish, unprocessed, all types	O	O	O	frozen
Flour, stoneground	O	O	O	
Fruit & nut mix, exotic	O	H	O	
Fruits of the forest drink	O	H	F	chilled
Ginger, ground	O	O	O	
Golden syrup	O	H	O	
Grapefruit juice	O	O	O	long life
Grapefruit juice, concentrated	O	O	O	frozen
Grapefruit segments in natural juice	O	O	O	can
Grapefruit segments in syrup	O	H	O	can
Haddock mornay	L	L	O	frozen
Hazelnuts	O	O	O	
Honey, all countries of origin	H	H	O	
Hot cross bun, wholemeal	O	L	O	
Ice cream choc ice, mint flavour	O	H	O	
Ice cream chocolate flake	O	H	O	
Ice cream dairy cones	O	H	O	
Ice cream, strawberry sorbet	O	H	F	
Ice lollies, choc nut	O	H	O	
Ice lollies, natural grapefruit	O	H	F	
Ice lollies, natural orange	O	H	O	

TESCO	Salt	Sugar	Flavour	Packaging
Irish Stew	L	O	O	can
Jaffa orange juice, pure	O	O	O	chilled
Lentils	O	O	O	dried
Lentils, green Continental	O	O	O	dried
Loganberries, in syrup	O	H	O	can
Malted chocolate drink	L	H	F	
Malted drink	L	H	O	
Margarine, premier	H	O	F	
Margarine, salt-free	O	O	F	
Margarine, soft	H	O	F	
Margarine, sunflower	H	O	F	
Margarine, supersoft	H	O	F	
Margarine, table	H	O	F	
Mayonnaise	O	L	F	
Meringue flan	O	H	O	
Meringue nest	O	H	O	
Milk, evaporated	O	O	O	can
Milk, full cream	O	O	O	long life
Milk, pasteurized	O	O	O	fresh
Milk, semi skimmed	O	O	O	long life
Milk, semi skimmed	O	O	O	fresh

TESCO	Salt	Sugar	Flavour	Packaging
Milk, skimmed	O	O	O	dried
Milk, skimmed	O	O	O	long life
Milk, skimmed	O	O	O	fresh
Mint imperials	O	H	O	
Mint, sparkling	O	H	O	
Mixed fruit drink	O	H	O	long life
Mixed spice, ground	O	O	O	
Muffins, wholemeal	L	L	O	
Mushrooms, Continental	L	O	O	can
Mushrooms, sliced	H	O	O	can
Mushrooms, whole button	H	O	O	can
Mushrooms, whole button	O	O	O	frozen
Mussels	O	O	O	frozen
Nutmeg, ground	O	O	O	
Nuts & raisins with chocolate chips	O	O	O	
Nuts & raisins, mixed	O	H	O	
Nuts & raisins, mixed, no salt added	O	O	O	
Nuts, Brazil	O	O	O	
Nuts, cashews	O	O	O	
Nuts, cashews, roasted salted	L	O	O	
Nuts, cut, mixed	O	O	O	

TESCO	Salt	Sugar	Flavour	Packaging
Nuts, monkey	O	O	O	
Nuts, salted mixed	H	O	O	
Oat cereal, instant	O	O	O	
Oil, cooking	O	O	O	
Oil, corn	O	O	O	
Oil, ground nut	O	O	O	
Oil, olive	O	O	O	
Oil, sunflower	H	O	O	
Olives, stuffed	O	O	O	
Onion rings in batter	O	O	O	frozen
Orange & pineapple juice	O	O	O	long life
Orange juice, concentrated	O	O	O	frozen
Orange juice, freshly squeezed	O	O	O	chilled
Orange juice, pure	O	O	O	chilled
Paprika	O	O	O	
Pasta verdi, all types	O	O	O	
Pasta with egg, all types	O	O	O	
Pasta, durum wheat only	O	O	O	
Pasta, quick cook with egg, all types	O	O	O	
Paste, salmon & shrimp	L	O	O	jar
Paste, sardine & tomato	L	O	F	jar

TESCO	Salt	Sugar	Flavour	Packaging
Pâté, smoked mackerel & onion	H	O	O	
Pâté, smoked trout	H	O	O	
Pâté, tuna	H	O	O	
Peaches in natural juice	O	O	O	can
Peaches in syrup	O	H	O	can
Peanut butter, crunchy	L	L	F	
Peanut butter, smooth	L	L	F	
Peanut crackle	L	H	O	
Peanuts & raisins, blanched	O	O	O	
Peanuts & raisins, milk chocolate	O	H	O	
Peanuts, raw	O	O	O	
Peanuts, salted	H	O	O	
Pears in natural juice	O	O	O	can
Pears in syrup	O	H	O	can
Peas, garden	O	O	O	frozen
Peas, green split	O	O	O	
Peas, marrowfat	O	O	O	
Peas, mint	O	O	O	frozen
Peas, yellow split	O	O	O	
Pepper, black, ground	O	O	O	
Pepper, black, whole	O	O	O	

TESCO	Salt	Sugar	Flavour	Packaging
Pepper, white, ground	O	O	O	
Peppermint flavouring	O	O	O	
Peppers, diced, mixed	O	O	O	frozen
Petit pois	L	L	O	frozen
Petit pois	L	L	O	can
Petit pois & baby carrots	O	H	O	jar
Pie filling, apple	O	O	O	can
Pineapple in natural juice	O	H	O	can
Pineapple in syrup	O	O	O	can
Pineapple juice	O	O	O	long life
Pineapple juice, pure	O	O	O	chilled
Pistachios, salted	H	H	O	
Plums, golden, in syrup	O	O	O	can
Potato shell	H	O	O	
Potatoes, new	L	O	O	can
Potatoes, new, Jersey	L	O	O	can
Prawns	H	L	O	frozen
Prunes in syrup	O	O	O	can
Prunes, no need to soak	O	H	O	dried
Puffed rice	H	H	O	
Raisins, seedless	O	O	O	dried

TESCO	Salt	Sugar	Flavour	Packaging
Raisins, yogurt coated	L	H	O	
Ratatouille	H	L	O	can
Ratatouille vegetables, mixed	O	O	O	frozen
Ready meal, beef & dumpling	L	O	F	chilled
Ready meal, beef hotpot	L	O	F	chilled
Ready meal, beef Provençal	L	L	O	chilled
Ready meal, Chilli con Carne	L	L	O	chilled
Ready meal, cauliflower cheese	L	O	O	chilled
Ready meal, cheese & potato bake	L	O	F	chilled
Ready meal, farmhouse casserole	L	L	F	chilled
Ready meal, pork Parisien	H	O	F	chilled
Ready meal, spicy vegetable	H	H	O	chilled
Relish, onion	O	O	O	
Rice, Basmati	O	O	O	
Rice, brown	O	O	O	frozen
Rice, brown & vegetables	O	O	O	
Rice, easy-to-cook	O	O	O	
Rice, ground	O	O	O	
Rice, long grain	O	O	O	
Sago	O	O	O	
Salad, apple, peach & nut	L	L	O	4-pot

TESCO	Salt	Sugar	Flavour	Packaging
Salad, bean, in wine vinegar	L	L	O	can
Salad, coleslaw	L	L	O	4 pot
Salad, coleslaw	L	L	O	pre-packed
Salad, coleslaw, curried	L	L	O	pre-packed
Salad, coleslaw, in low calorie dressing	L	L	O	pre-packed
Salad, coleslaw, in vinaigrette	L	L	O	pre-packed
Salad, coleslaw, premier	L	L	O	pre-packed
Salad, Florida	L	L	O	pre-packed
Salad, mixed, in French dressing	L	L	O	pre-packed
Salad, potato	L	L	O	pre-packed
Salad, potato & chives	L	L	O	4 pot
Salad, potato & chives	L	L	O	pre-packed
Salad, potato, in low calorie dressing	L	L	O	pre-packed
Salad, vegetable	L	L	O	4 pot
Salad, vegetable	L	L	O	pre-packed
Salad, vegetable, in low calorie dressing	L	L	O	pre-packed
Salad, Waldorf	O	H	O	pre-packed
Satsuma segments in syrup	L	L	O	can
Sauce, Bolognese	O	H	O	jar
Sauce, cranberry	H	H	F	
Sauce, horseradish				

TESCO	Salt	Sugar	Flavour	Packaging
Sauce, Napolitana	L	H	O	jar
Sauce, tartare	H	H	F	
Scotch porridge oats	O	O	O	
Scotch porridge oats with bran	O	O	O	
Semolina	O	O	O	
Sesame nut crunch	H	O	O	
Soup, cream of tomato	H	L	O	can
Spaghetti hoops	H	L	O	can
Spaghetti lengths	H	L	O	can
Spaghetti letters	H	L	O	can
Spinach, leaf	O	O	O	frozen
Spread, low fat	L	O	F	
Spread, low fat dairy	H	O	F	
Stuffing, country herb	H	O	O	
Stuffing, parsley & thyme	H	O	O	
Stuffing, sage & onion	H	O	O	
Sugar flakes	O	I	O	
Sweetcorn	H	O	O	frozen
Sweetcorn	H	L	O	can
Sweetcorn & peppers	H	L	O	can
Swiss-style breakfast cereal	L	H	O	

TESCO	Salt	Sugar	Flavour	Packaging
Tapioca	O	O	O	
Tea, all types	O	O	O	
Toffee roll, chocolate covered	L	H	F	
Toffee, bon-bon	L	H	F	
Toffee, brazil nut	L	H	F	
Toffee, cream	L	H	F	
Tomato juice	O	O	O	long life
Tomato purée	L	O	O	can
Tomatoes, chopped	L	O	O	can
Tomatoes, plum	L	O	O	can
Tropical drink	O	H	O	chilled
Turkey slices, prime	H	O	O	pre-packed
Vegetables, casserole mix	O	O	O	frozen
Vegetables, fresh farmhouse, mixed	O	O	O	frozen
Vegetables, fresh manor, mixed	O	O	O	frozen
Vegetables, fresh Parisienne, mixed	O	O	O	frozen
Vegetables, mixed	O	O	O	frozen
Vegetables, mixed	L	O	O	can
Vegetables, special, mixed	O	O	O	frozen
Vegetables, summer, mixed	L	O	O	frozen
Vinegar, red wine	O	O	O	can

TESCO	Salt	Sugar	Flavour	Packaging
Vinegar, white wine	O	O	O	
Walnuts, shelled	O	O	O	
Water, natural, Cwm Dale	O	O	O	
Water, natural, Highland Spring	O	O	O	
Water, sparkling, Cwm Dale	O	O	O	
Water, sparkling, Highland Spring	O	O	O	
Wholemeal bran biscuit	H	L	F	
Wholemeal shortbread finger	L	H	O	
Wholewheat cereal	H	L	O	
Wholewheat flakes	L	L	O	
Yogurt, French style, apricot	O	H	O	
Yogurt, French style, lemon	O	H	O	
Yogurt, French style, strawberry	O	H	O	
Yogurt, French style, vanilla	O	H	O	
Yogurt, low fat, black cherry	O	H	F	
Yogurt, low fat, coconut	O	H	F	
Yogurt, low fat, fruits of the forest	O	H	F	
Yogurt, low fat, hazelnut	O	H	F	
Yogurt, low fat, natural set	O	O	O	
Yogurt, low fat, natural stirred	O	O	O	
Yogurt, low fat, passion fruit & melon	O	H	F	

TESCO	Salt	Sugar	Flavour	Packaging
Yogurt, low fat, pear	O	H	F	
Yogurt, rich chocolate	O	H	O	

NOTES

NOTES

WAITROSE

Waitrose is committed to selling good wholesome foods and places strong emphasis on fresh fruits and vegetables, bread, fish and cereals. Processed long life foods, by their very nature, require some additives; but for two years we have been questioning even some of these. We now have over 100 additive-free products and many more which contain only natural additives.

Recent developments include additive-free fish fingers, cookies, biscuits, breakfast cereals, jams, ketchup, low calorie soup, soft drinks and most ready prepared meals. We have also commissioned a small pilot scheme for organically grown vegetables for this autumn, and already have organically grown mangetout, fennel and green beans in about 27 of our branches.

It must be said, however, that not all additives will disappear. Without preservatives, for example, some foods would deteriorate rapidly and that would have quite serious implications upon healthy eating from another point of view; but we are certainly making progress and intend to continue doing so. This exercise is a lengthy one and involves careful development of many recipes in order to determine the specifications for each product.

We have not listed products containing dried fruit in case the fruit bears a trace of sulphur dioxide which is used as a preservative. Waitrose declares sulphur dioxide on all its mueslis for this reason. However, you will find that very few other brands of muesli do, despite the fact that the fruit will have been treated in the same way. Where we have listed a dried fruit, such as California raisins, no sulphur dioxide has been used. For the same reason, we have not listed products which use ham as an added ingredient — e.g., cottage cheese with ham and pineapple, in case nitrites/nitrates might be present. This would not be indicated on the ingredients list.

WAITROSE	Salt	Sugar	Flavour	Packaging
Apple & cherry juice	O	O	O	long life
Apple juice	O	O	O	long life
Apple juice, pure	O	O	O	chilled
Apple juice, sparkling English	O	O	O	bottle
Apple slices	O	O	O	can
Apricots in natural juice	O	H	O	can
Apricots in syrup	H	O	O	can
Artichokes	H	O	O	can
Asparagus, Canadian green	H	O	O	can
Asparagus, white (four types)	L	L	O	can
Aubergine gratin	L	H	X	fresh
Baked roll, raspberry	L	H	X	film wrapped
Baked roll, treacle	L	O	O	can
Barley, pearl	O	O	O	can
Beans, baked	H	L	O	can
Beans, baked in apple juice	H	O	O	film wrapped
Beans, barbecue	H	L	F	can
Beans, butter	O	O	O	film wrapped
Beans, cut green	H	O	O	can
Beans, haricot	O	L	O	film wrapped
Beans, red kidney	H	H	O	can

WAITROSE	Salt	Sugar	Flavour	Packaging
Beans, sliced green	O	O	O	frozen
Beans, whole green	O	O	O	frozen
Beans, whole green	H	O	O	can
Beef drink	H	O	O	
Beef Vindaloo	H	O	O	frozen
Beefburgers	H	O	O	frozen
Beetroot, sliced in sweet vinegar	L	H	O	
Beetroot, sliced in vinegar	L	H	F	
Biscuits, almond	L	H	F	
Biscuits, breaktime (milk)	L	H	O	
Biscuits, breaktime (plain)	L	H	F	
Biscuits, butter	L	H	O	
Biscuits, butter crunch	H	H	F	
Biscuits, digestive	L	H	O	
Biscuits, ginger creams	L	H	O	
Biscuits, milk chocolate digestives	L	H	F	
Biscuits, plain chocolate digestives	L	H	F	
Biscuits, tea finger	L	H	O	
Biscuits, treacle creams	L	H	O	
Bran flakes	H	H	F	
Bread, farmhouse white sliced	H	O	O	pre-packed

WAITROSE	Salt	Sugar	Flavour	Packaging
Bread, soft malted wheat	X	X	O	pre-packed
Bread, soft wholemeal	H	O	O	pre-packed
Broccoli	O	O	O	frozen
Brussels sprouts	O	O	O	frozen
Burger steaks	L	O	O	frozen
Butter, Devonshire	H	O	O	
Butter, dairy blend	H	O	O	
Butter, home produced	H	O	O	
Butter, Normandy unsalted	O	O	O	
Buttermilk	O	O	O	
Cake, angel sandwich	L	H	X	pre-packed
Cake, cherry Genoa	L	H	X	pre-packed
Cake, chocolate sandwich	L	H	X	pre-packed
Cake, coconut sandwich	L	H	X	pre-packed
Cake, coconut (round)	L	H	X	pre-packed
Cake, date & walnut	L	H	X	pre-packed
Cake, French jam sandwich	L	H	X	pre-packed
Cake, iced fruit	L	H	X	pre-packed
Cake, lemon iced Madeira sandwich	L	H	X	pre-packed
Cake, light fruit	L	H	X	pre-packed
Cake, Madeira slice	L	H	X	pre-packed

WAITROSE	Salt	Sugar	Flavour	Packaging
Cake, Madeira with buttercream filling	L	H	X	pre-packed
Cake, Madeira (round)	L	H	X	pre-packed
Cake, paradise	L	H	X	pre-packed
Cake, rich fruit	L	H	X	pre-packed
Cake, walnut layer	L	H	X	pre-packed
Cake, whole sultana	L	H	X	pre-packed
Cakes, Chorley	L	H	X	
Cakes, Eccles	L	X	X	pre-packed
Capellini	O	O	O	dried
Carrots	H	L	O	can
Carrots, baby	H	L	O	can
Carrots, finger	O	O	O	frozen
Carrots, sliced	H	L	O	can
Cauliflower	O	O	O	frozen
Cauliflower cheese	L	O	O	foil tray/fresh
Cauliflower/peas/mushroom, stir fry	O	O	O	frozen
Celery hearts	L	O	O	can
Cheese, Alpsberg	H	O	O	
Cheese, Belle des Champs	H	O	O	
Cheese, Caerphilly farmhouse	H	O	O	
Cheese, Camembert	H	O	O	

WAITROSE	Salt	Sugar	Flavour	Packaging
Cheese, Cheddar home produced	H	O	O	
Cheese, Cheddar, Canadian	H	O	O	
Cheese, Cheddar, English	H	O	O	
Cheese, Cheddar, English with walnuts	H	O	O	
Cheese, Cheddar, extra mild English	H	O	O	
Cheese, Cheddar, farmhouse	H	O	O	
Cheese, Cheddar, farmhouse matured	H	O	O	
Cheese, Cheddar, farmhouse Somerset	H	O	O	
Cheese, Cheddar, Irish	H	O	O	
Cheese, Cheddar, red English	H	O	F	
Cheese, Cheddar, Scottish matured	H	O	O	
Cheese, Cheddar, vegetarian	H	O	O	
Cheese, chèvre (goat)	H	O	O	
Cheese, cottage	H	O	O	
Cheese, cottage with Cheddar	H	O	O	
Cheese, cottage with onion & chives	H	O	O	
Cheese, cottage with prawns	H	O	O	
Cheese, cream with chives	H	O	O	
Cheese, curd	H	O	O	
Cheese, Danish blue extra mature	H	O	O	
Cheese, Danish blue mature	H	O	O	

WAITROSE	Salt	Sugar	Flavour	Packaging
Cheese, Danish blue mild	H	O	O	
Cheese, Danish Samsoe	H	O	O	
Cheese, Dolcelatte	H	O	O	
Cheese, double Gloucester farmhouse	H	O	O	
Cheese, Dutch Gouda	H	O	O	
Cheese, double Gloucester with chives & onions	H	O	O	
Cheese, Emmentaler	H	O	O	
Cheese, French Brie	H	O	O	
Cheese, French Brie supreme	H	O	O	
Cheese, German blue Brie	H	O	O	
Cheese, German Brie with mushrooms	H	O	O	
Cheese, Havarti slices	H	O	O	
Cheese, Lancashire	H	O	O	
Cheese, Lys bleu	H	O	O	
Cheese, Parmesan, Italian	H	O	O	
Cheese, red Cheshire	H	O	O	
Cheese, red Leicester, farmhouse	H	O	O	
Cheese, Somerset Brie	H	O	O	
Cheese, St Paulin	H	O	O	
Cheese, Stilton, blue	H	O	O	
Cheese, Stilton, white	H	O	O	

WAITROSE	Salt	Sugar	Flavour	Packaging
Cheese, sage Derby	H	O	O	
Cheese, spread, processed	H	O	O	
Cheese, spread, processed with prawns	H	O	O	
Cheese, Wensleydale	H	O	O	
Cheese, white Cheshire	H	O	O	
Chick peas	H	O	O	can
Chicken Biryani	H	O	O	frozen
Chicken breast fillets	L	L	O	pre-packed
Chicken Chow Mein	O	L	O	pre-packed
Chicken Cordon Bleu	L	L	O	pre-packed
Chicken Kiev	H	O	O	frozen
Chicken Masala	H	O	O	foil tray/fresh
Chicken Masala	H	O	O	frozen
Chicken Moghlai	L	L	O	pre-packed
Chicken nibbles	L	O	O	pre-packed
Chicken Romane	H	O	O	delicatessen
Chicken spring roll	H	O	O	frozen
Chicken Tikka Makhanwala	L	L	O	pre-packed
Chicken, Goujons	L	O	O	frozen
Chilli con Carne	O	O	O	foil tray/fresh

WAITROSE	Salt	Sugar	Flavour	Packaging
Choc & nut cookies	L	H	F	
Chocolate Brazils	O	H	F	
Chocolate chip & orange cookies	L	H	F	frozen
Chocolate chip cookies	L	H	O	
Chocolate chip shortbread	O	H	O	
Chocolate gingers	O	H	F	
Chocolate thin mint crisps	L	H	F	
Chutney, apricot & ginger	H	H	O	
Chutney, mango	L	H	O	
Chutney, onion	L	H	O	
Chutney, tomato	L	H	O	
Coconut cookies	L	H	O	
Coconut crumble creams	L	H	F	
Coconut rings	L	H	F	
Cod & broccoli mornay	L	O	O	foil tray/fresh
Cod fillets in natural crumb with parsley	O	L	O	pre-packed
Coffee bags, Columbian	O	O	O	
Coffee bags, Kenyan	O	O	O	
Coffee beans, Columbian	O	O	O	
Coffee beans, Continental	O	O	O	
Coffee beans, French	O	O	O	

WAITROSE	Salt	Sugar	Flavour	Packaging
Coffee beans, Kenyan	o	o	o	packet
Coffee beans, mountain	o	o	o	
Coffee granules, dark	o	o	o	
Coffee granules, medium	o	o	o	
Coffee granules, rich-roast	o	o	o	
Coffee powder, full-flavoured	o	o	o	
Coffee powder, mild	o	o	o	
Coffee, Columbian	o	o	o	
Coffee, Continental filter	o	o	o	
Coffee, Continental freeze-dried	o	o	o	can
Coffee, choice blend	o	o	o	
Coffee, decaffeinated	o	o	o	
Coffee, French filter	o	o	o	
Coffee, French medium	o	o	o	
Coffee, ground Continental	o	o	o	
Coffee, ground Kenyan	o	o	o	
Coffee, instant decaffeinated	o	o	o	
Coffee, Kenyan filter	o	o	o	
Coffee, Maragogype	o	o	o	
Coffee, mild-roast	o	o	o	
Coffee, mountain filter	o	o	o	

WAITROSE	Salt	Sugar	Flavour	Packaging
Coffee, mountain freeze-dried	O	O	O	
Coffee, supreme freeze-dried	O	O	O	
Coffee, Vienna	O	O	O	
Coffee/chicory	O	O	O	
Conserve, apricot	O	H	O	jar
Conserve, black cherry	O	H	O	jar
Conserve, blackcurrant	O	H	O	jar
Conserve, ginger	O	H	O	jar
Conserve, morello cherry	O	H	O	jar
Conserve, raspberry	O	H	O	jar
Conserve, strawberry	O	H	O	jar
Corn on the cob	O	O	O	frozen
Cornflakes	H	H	O	
Cornflour	O	O	O	
Cornish pasty, premium	L	O	O	delicatessen
Courgettes Provençales	L	O	O	foil tray/fresh
Courgettes/mushroom/corn, stir fry	O	O	O	frozen
Cream crackers	H	O	O	
Cream, clotted	O	O	O	
Cream, double	O	O	O	
Cream, extra thick double	O	O	O	

WAITROSE	Salt	Sugar	Flavour	Packaging
Cream, half	O	O	O	
Cream, single	O	O	O	
Cream, soured	O	O	O	
Cream, spooning	O	O	O	
Cream, whipping	O	O	O	
Crespolini	L	O	O	delicatessen
Crumble, apple	O	H	O	foil tray
Crumble, gooseberry	O	H	O	foil tray
Crunchy cookies	L	H	O	
Custard creams	L	O	O	
Dal Masala	H	I	F	frozen
Digestive finger creams	L	O	O	
Dolmades	L	H	O	delicatessen
Éclairs	O	O	F	frozen
Fish cakes	I	I	F	frozen
Fish fingers, cod fillet	L	O	O	frozen
Fish fingers, minced cod	L	O	O	frozen
Five fruit cocktail juice	O	O	O	long life
Flour, plain	O	O	O	
Flour, plain superfine	O	O	O	
Flour, self raising	O	O	O	

WAITROSE	Salt	Sugar	Flavour	Packaging
Flour, self raising superfine	O	O	O	
Flour, strong white bread	O	O	O	
Flour, wholewheat	O	O	O	
Four fruit cocktail juice	O	O	O	long life
Fruit & nuts, exotic	L	L	O	
Ginger cookies	L	H	F	
Ginger snaps	L	H	F	
Ginger thins	L	H	O	
Grape & blackcurrant juice	O	O	O	long life
Grape juice, red	O	O	O	bottle
Grape juice, white	O	O	O	bottle
Grapefruit in juice	O	O	O	can
Grapefruit juice	O	O	O	long life
Grapefruit juice, pure	O	O	O	chilled
Haddock Goujons	L	L	O	pre-packed
Haricots verts	L	O	F	can
Highland shorties	H	H	O	
Honey, Australian clear	L	O	O	jar
Honey, Australian set	O	O	O	jar
Honey, Canadian	O	O	O	jar
Honey, Chinese	O	O	O	jar

WAITROSE	Salt	Sugar	Flavour	Packaging
Honey, cut comb	O	O	O	jar
Honey, English	O	O	O	jar
Honey, Greek	O	O	O	jar
Honey, Mexican	O	O	O	jar
Honey, Tasmanian	H	O	O	jar
Houmous	O	O	O	delicatessen
Jaffa orange juice	L	O	F	chilled
Jam creams	O	H	O	
Jam, apricot	O	H	O	jar
Jam, apricot, reduced sugar	O	H	O	jar
Jam, blackcurrant, reduced sugar	O	H	O	jar
Jam, damson	O	H	O	jar
Jam, morello cherry, reduced sugar	O	H	O	jar
Jam, pineapple	O	H	O	jar
Jam, raspberry	O	H	O	jar
Jam, raspberry, reduced sugar	O	H	O	jar
Jam, Swiss black cherry, reduced sugar	O	H	O	jar
Jam, strawberry, reduced sugar	O	H	O	jar
Jelly, blackcurrant	O	H	O	jar
Lamb boulangère	L	O	O	foil tray/fresh
Lamb curry	L	O	O	foil tray/fresh

WAITROSE	Salt	Sugar	Flavour	Packaging
Lamb rogan josh	H	O	O	frozen
Lattice flans	L	O	O	frozen
Légumes mornay	L	O	O	foil tray/fresh
Lemon cheese	O	H	O	jar
Lemon curd	O	H	O	jar
Lentils	O	O	O	film wrapped
Macaroni, Italian	O	O	O	dried
Macaroni, wholewheat	O	O	O	dried
Malted drink	O	O	O	
Mandarins in juice	O	O	O	can
Mandarins in syrup	O	H	O	can
Margarine, blended	H	O	O	block in foil
Margarine, blended soft	H	L	O	carton
Margarine, soya soft	H	L	O	carton
Margarine, sunflower soft	O	L	O	carton
Marmalade, fresh grapefruit	O	H	O	jar
Marmalade, fresh orange	O	H	O	jar
Marmalade, orange (thin cut)	O	H	O	jar
Marmalade, orange, reduced sugar	O	H	O	jar
Marmalade, three fruits	O	H	O	jar
Marzipan, white	O	H	O	

WAITROSE	Salt	Sugar	Flavour	Packaging
Mayonnaise	L	L	F	
Mayonnaise, lemon	L	L	F	
Milk chocolate orange wafer fingers	L	H	F	
Milk chocolate wafer fingers	L	H	F	
Milk, Channel Isle	O	O	O	can
Milk, evaporated	O	O	O	
Milk, full cream	O	O	O	
Milk, goat	O	O	O	
Milk, semi skimmed	O	O	O	
Milk, skimmed	O	O	O	
Milk, spray-dried instant powder	O	O	O	
Minced beef Bolognese	L	H	X	fresh
Mince pies, puff	L	H	X	fresh
Mince pies, shortcrust	L	H	X	can
Mince pies, wholemeal	L	H	X	frozen
Mini rolls with strawberry conserve and buttercream	L	H	X	
Mini rolls, choc covered with raspberry conserve	L	H	X	
Mini rolls, choc covered with vanilla filling	L	H	X	
Mint creams	O	H	F	
Mint imperials	O	H	F	

WAITROSE	Salt	Sugar	Flavour	Packaging
Moussaka	L	O	O	foil tray/fresh
Mushrooms	H	O	O	can
Mussels in tomato sauce	L	L	F	fresh
Nuts & raisins, mixed	O	O	O	
Nuts, pistachio	H	O	O	
Oat flake & honey cookies	L	H	O	
Oil, corn	O	O	O	
Oil, groundnut	O	O	O	
Oil, olive	O	O	O	
Oil, safflower	O	O	O	
Oil, soya vegetable	O	O	O	
Oil, sunflower	O	O	O	
Oil, vegetable blended	O	O	O	
Onion Bhaji	L	O	O	delicatessen
Orange juice	O	O	O	long life
Orange juice, pure	O	O	O	chilled
Orange/apricot drink	O	O	O	chilled
Pakora	L	H	O	delicatessen
Pancake, cheese, ham & mushroom	L	O	O	fresh
Party twigs	H	O	O	
Passata	L	O	O	can

WAITROSE	Salt	Sugar	Flavour	Packaging
Pasta bows	O	O	O	dried
Pasta quills	O	O	O	dried
Pasta shells	O	O	O	dried
Pasta tubes	O	O	O	dried
Pasta twists	O	O	O	dried
Pasta wheels	O	O	O	dried
Pavlova, chocolate	O	H	O	frozen
Peaches & pears in syrup	O	H	O	can
Peaches in syrup	L	H	O	can
Peaches, sliced in syrup	H	H	O	can
Peanut butter cookies	H	H	O	frozen
Peanut butter, crunchy	O	H	O	jar
Peanut butter, smooth	H	H	O	jar
Peanuts & raisins	O	O	O	
Peanuts, salted	O	O	O	
Peanuts, shelled	O	O	O	
Pears in natural juice	O	O	O	can
Pears in syrup	O	H	O	can
Peas & carrots, mixed	L	L	O	can
Peas, dried	O	O	O	film wrapped
Peas, garden	O	O	O	frozen

WAITROSE	Salt	Sugar	Flavour	Packaging
Peas, mint	O	O	O	frozen
Peas, split	O	O	O	film wrapped
Peas/corn/pepper	O	O	O	frozen
Pepper, chopped mixed	O	O	O	frozen
Peppers, red	H	H	F	can
Petit beurre (milk & plain chocolate)	L	O	O	
Petit pois	O	L	O	frozen
Petit pois	H	H	O	can
Petticoat tails	L	H	O	
Piccalilli, mustard	H	H	O	
Piccalilli, sweet	H	O	O	frozen
Pie, chicken/ham/mushroom	L	H	O	
Pie, lattice with summer fruits filling	L	H	X	
Pie, lattice with tropical fruits filling	L	O	X	frozen
Pie, minced beef	L	O	O	frozen
Pie, steak & kidney	L	H	O	
Pie, wholemeal apple mini	L	H	X	
Pies, apple	L	H	X	
Pies, blackcurrant shortcrust	L	H	X	
Pies, blackcurrant wholemeal	L	H	X	
Pineapple juice	O	O	O	long life

WAITROSE	Salt	Sugar	Flavour	Packaging
Pineapple juice, pure	O	O	O	chilled
Pineapple pieces in natural juice	O	O	O	can
Pineapple pieces in syrup	O	H	O	can
Pineapple slices in syrup	O	H	O	can
Pittas, traditional	X	X	X	pre-packed
Pittas, wholemeal traditional	X	X	X	pre-packed
Pizza, campagnola	L	O	O	frozen
Pizza, French bread ham/mushroom	L	O	O	frozen
Pizza, French bread tomato/cheese	L	O	O	frozen
Pizza, Marinara	L	O	O	frozen
Pizza, pepperoni	H	O	O	frozen
Pizzas, 10 party	L	O	O	frozen
Plaice & prawn véronique	L	L	O	foil tray/fresh
Plaice fillets in natural crumb with parsley	L	L	O	pre-packed
Plaice with mornay filling	L	O	O	fresh
Plaice, breaded	O	H	O	frozen
Plain chocolate	L	H	F	
Plain chocolate wafer fingers	O	H	F	
Plain chocolate with hazelnuts	H	H	F	
Pork sausage meat	O	O	O	frozen
Porridge oats	O	O	O	

215

WAITROSE	Salt	Sugar	Flavour	Packaging
Potato dauphinoise	L	O	O	foil tray/fresh
Potato lamb cutlet	L	O	O	delicatessen
Potato, cheese & asparagus pancakes	L	O	O	foil tray/fresh
Potatoes, new (except Jersey)	H	O	O	can
Prawn, smoked salmon & tuna bap	L	O	O	fresh
Quiche, Stilton	O	O	O	delicatessen
Quiche, Swiss cheese & broccoli	O	O	O	delicatessen
Raisins, California	O	O	O	dried
Ratatouille	O	L	O	frozen
Ratatouille	L	O	O	can
Ratatouille	L	H	O	foil tray/fresh
Rice crunchies	H	O	O	dried
Rice, American long grain	O	H	O	can
Rice, creamed	O	O	O	dried
Rice, easy to cook	O	O	O	dried
Rice, flaked	O	O	O	dried
Rice, long grain brown	O	O	O	dried
Rice, pilau	L	O	O	dried
Rice, pudding	O	O	O	dried
Rice, risotto	O	O	O	dried
Rice, stir fry	L	O	O	foil tray/fresh

WAITROSE	Salt	Sugar	Flavour	Packaging
Salad, apricot & nut	L	O	O	delicatessen
Salad, carrot & nut	L	L	O	delicatessen
Salad, courgettes, wheat & almond	O	L	O	delicatessen
Salad, healthy fruit & honey	L	O	O	delicatessen
Salad, Mexican bean	L	L	O	delicatessen
Salad, Mexican style	L	L	O	delicatessen
Salad, pepper	L	O	O	can
Salad, potato/mint	L	O	O	delicatessen
Samosa, chicken	L	O	O	delicatessen
Samosa, lamb	L	O	O	delicatessen
Samosa, vegetable	L	O	O	delicatessen
Samosa, vegetable	H	O	O	frozen
Sausage rolls, 6	H	O	O	frozen
Sausages, thin pork	H	O	O	frozen
Sausages, thick pork	H	L	O	frozen
Scampi in crispy coating	L	O	O	pre-packed
Seafood salad	O	O	O	delicatessen
Semolina	H	O	O	dried
Sesame crackers	L	O	O	
Shortbread fingers	L	H	F	
Smoked haddock savoury bake	L	O	O	foil tray/fresh

WAITROSE	Salt	Sugar	Flavour	Packaging
Sole Goujons	L	L	O	pre-packed
Sorbet, lemon	O	H	O	frozen
Soup, asparagus low calorie	L	O	O	
Soup, Cornish crab bisque	L	L	O	
Soup, clam chowder	L	O	O	
Soup, cream of tomato	L	L	O	can
Soup, lobster bisque	L	L	O	
Soup, tomato low calorie	L	O	O	
Soutsoukakia	O	O	O	delicatessen
Spaghetti	O	O	O	dried
Spaghetti verdi	O	O	O	dried
Spaghetti, Italian	O	O	O	dried
Spaghetti, wholewheat	O	O	O	dried
Spare ribs	L	L	O	foil tray/fresh
Spicy meat balls	L	O	O	foil tray/fresh
Spinach	L	O	O	can
Sponge fingers	L	H	F	
Sponge with black cherry conserve & buttercream filling	L	H	X	
Sponge with blackcurrant conserve & buttercream filling	L	H	X	

218

WAITROSE	Salt	Sugar	Flavour	Packaging
Sponge with lemon cheese & buttercream filling	L	H	X	
Sponge with strawberry conserve & buttercream filling	L	H	X	
Sponge, choc with black cherry conserve & buttercream	L	H	X	
Sponge, choc with buttercream filling	L	H	X	
Spread, low fat	H	O	O	carton
Sprouts, button	O	O	O	frozen
Stuffing mix, country herb	H	O	O	packet
Stuffing mix, parsley, thyme & lemon	H	O	F	packet
Stuffing mix, sage & onion	H	O	F	packet
Sultana & spice creams	L	O	F	
Sweet & sour chicken	L	H	O	frozen
Sweetcorn	O	H	O	frozen
Sweetcorn	L	O	O	can
Sweetcorn with peppers	L	O	O	can
Sweetcorn, creamed	L	O	O	can
Swiss roll, chocolate covered	O	H	F	
Tagliatelle	L	O	O	dried
Tagliatelle Niçoise	L	O	O	foil tray/fresh

WAITROSE	Salt	Sugar	Flavour	Packaging
Tea bags, Assam	O	O	O	
Tea bags, breakfast	O	O	O	
Tea bags, Ceylon	O	O	O	
Tea bags, Earl Grey	O	O	O	
Tea, breakfast	O	O	O	
Tea, Darjeeling	O	O	O	
Tea, Earl Grey	O	O	O	
Tea, Jasmine	O	O	O	
Tea, Kemun China	O	O	O	
Tea, Kenya	O	O	O	
Tea, Lapsang	O	O	O	
Tea, taste of Assam	O	O	O	
Tea, taste of Ceylon	O	O	O	
Tea, taste of Kenya	O	O	O	
Three fruit cocktail juice	O	O	F	long life
Toffees, Devon	O	H	O	
Tomato juice	H	O	O	long life
Tomato ketchup	L	H	F	jar/tube/can
Tomato paste	L	O	O	jar
Tomato paste with basil	O	L	O	
Tomatoes	O	O	O	can

WAITROSE	Salt	Sugar	Flavour	Packaging
Tomatoes, crushed	L	O	O	can
Treacle cookies	L	H	O	
Trifle sponges	L	H	X	
Tropical fruit drink	O	H	O	chilled
Trout, fresh, with mushroom & onion stuffing	O	O	O	pre-packed
Trout, fresh, with savoury stuffing	L	O	O	pre-packed
Tzatziki	H	O	O	delicatessen
Vegetable pulao	O	O	O	frozen
Vegetables with prawns & rice, stir fry	L	O	O	frozen
Vegetables, macedoine of	O	O	O	can
Vegetables, mixed	H	O	O	frozen
Vegetables, mixed	O	O	O	can
Vegetables, stewpack	H	O	O	frozen
Wheat bran	L	H	O	
Wheat flakes	L	L	O	
Wholemeal shortbread fingers	L	H	O	
Wholewheat breakfast biscuits	H	L	O	
Yeast extract	O	O	F	
Yogurt, apple & sultana	O	H	O	carton
Yogurt, apricot	O	H	O	
Yogurt, banana	O	H	O	carton

WAITROSE	Salt	Sugar	Flavour	Packaging
Yogurt, black cherry	0	H	0	carton
Yogurt, black cherry extra thick	0	H	0	
Yogurt, blackberry & apple	0	H	0	carton
Yogurt, blackcurrant	0	H	0	carton
Yogurt, champagne rhubarb	0	H	0	carton
Yogurt, chocolate	0	H	0	carton
Yogurt, gooseberry	0	H	0	carton
Yogurt, hazelnut	0	H	0	carton
Yogurt, mandarin	0	H	0	carton
Yogurt, morello cherry	0	H	0	carton
Yogurt, natural set extra thick	0	H	0	carton
Yogurt, passion fruit & melon	0	H	0	carton
Yogurt, peach melba	0	H	0	carton
Yogurt, pineapple & coconut	0	H	0	carton
Yogurt, raspberry	0	H	0	carton
Yogurt, strawberry	0	H	0	carton
Yogurt, strawberry extra thick	0	H	0	carton
Yogurt, tropical fruit extra thick	0	H	0	carton
Yogurt, Victoria plum	0	H	0	carton
Yogurts, natural	0	H	0	carton